Harvest of Bread

Pictured above is the threshing outfit and crew operated by the author's father, Alex MacEwan at Brandon, Man. The photograph was taken in 1899 with Mr. MacEwan standing fourth from the left. The outfit was said to be the finest of its time in the region. It was the first steamer in Brandon district and the biggest separator (forty-four-inch) made at the time, equipped with the first feeder and blower seen in that part of the country.

Harvest of Bread

BY

Grant MacEwan

❧

PRAIRIE BOOKS

THE WESTERN PRODUCER
SASKATOON
1969

BOOKS BY THE SAME AUTHOR

The Science and Practice of Canadian Animal Husbandry
(In collaboration with A. H. Ewen)—1936

General Agriculture (In collaboration with A. H. Ewen)—1939

Breeds of Livestock in Canada—1941

Feeding Farm Animals—1945

Agriculture on Parade—1950

The Sodbusters—1946

Between the Red and the Rockies—1952

Eye Opener Bob—1957

Calgary Cavalcade—1958

Fifty Mighty Men—1958

John Ware's Cow Country—1960

Blazing the Old Cattle Trails—1962

Hoofprints and Hitchingposts—1964

Entrusted To My Care—1966

Poking Into Politics—1966

West to the Sea (In collaboration with Maxwell Foran)—1968

DEDICATION

*To the memory of my father who pioneered
in threshing with steam power and, ultimately,
saw the wheat crop on his western land being
harvested by self-propelled combines.*

PREFACE

The account of development in the great wheat industry is something with which every westerner — and, indeed, every Canadian — should be familiar. In large measure, it is the story of the country because the growth of wheat production and the history of Midwestern Canada are intertwined inseparably.

It was noted in Canada's Centennial Year that wheat could furnish the best of all western success stories. It was agreed that the story should be written. Now it can be added that this particular grain crop, which played the vital part in area development and plays no less essential a part in present-day economy, will be the means of a leading world role for Canada in the years ahead.

The following chapters, presented in general terms and with limited detail, were prepared for general readers more than for advanced scholars and specialists. The subject is big and challenging, and it is hoped that other writers will be attracted to it.

As a native son of western soil, it should not be surprising that the work of recording this part of the wheat story brought satisfaction and pleasure. My gratitude goes to those who furnished help and encouragement.

Edmonton, Alberta,   G. MacE.
September, 1968.

TABLE OF CONTENTS

LIST OF ILLUSTRATIONS

INTRODUCTION

Instead of writing a conventional introduction which would stand a chance of never being read, I decided to reproduce a letter which contains just about all the sentiment I would wish to convey. I hope my kind neighbor to whom it was addressed will not mind the public exposure of some private correspondence.

"My Dear Neighbor:

No praise is too generous for the person who makes good bread. My thanks for the loaf of homemade goodness delivered yesterday. Its texture, flavor and aroma marked it as something fit for the gods. When master hands are brought to flour, from Canadian wheat, the result can be almost divine. And, of course, the atmosphere of a farm kitchen like yours adds its own mysterious enrichment.

As I ate thick slices—perfect companions for good butter and honey —I thought of the history of wheat and flour in this land. I thought of David Fife and Charles Saunders and Seager Wheeler and a score of others who figured prominently in the struggle to make wheat the greatest thing in Canadian achievement. I thought of the disappointments and heartaches as well as the triumphs—the frozen crops, and the introduction of Marquis; the grasshoppers, and the new techniques to stop them; the droughts, and the development of irrigation; poor prices and better prices; the discouragement of poor samples, and then the championships; the rust, and the ingenuity brought to combat it.

It's a great story and there is more to it than most people realize. As I thought about it between bites of bread, I could hear the echo of scores of sounds familiar in Canadian industry—the anguished squeal of seed-drill discs needing lubrication; the motor roar of farm tractors; the shunting of loaded freight trains; the hum of terminal conveyors; the low-pitched voices of ocean-going vessels, carrying wheat and flour to other lands; the assembly-line whine in factories turning out agricultural equipment and the chatter of a million people employed in one capacity or another on the broadening stream of wheat; all of which touches my life and table in so many acceptable ways.

Thank God for the good soil yielding bread-abundance in Canada and thank you for the kind of bread that induces me to reach for another slice and then another.

Sincerely,

Grant MacEwan."

"A land wherein thou shalt eat bread without scarceness . . ."

—DEUTERONOMY 8:9

PART I

~ ◡ ~

THE TESTING TIMES

CHAPTER I

꩜

THE CANADIAN'S DEBT TO WHEAT

꩜

Every Canadian—not just the grower—owes a debt to wheat. Without the benefit of wheatlands, the western half of Canada would have been later by many years in breaking the grip of the fur trade. A transcontinental railway would have been long delayed and national progress, prosperity, and world prestige would have suffered serious retardation. The fact is that wheat accounted mainly for an area transformation unsurpassed in any other country.

Even with the rich treasure of good soil, there was delay. Two hundred years of fur trade did nothing to remove the prejudices and doubts concerning suitability of the land for wheat. One of the finest of the Creator's bequests could not escape controversy. If productivity of the plains had been as low as some early adventurers like Palliser[1] supposed, wheat would have held only small reason for hope, and Canadian development would have suffered the handicap of an economic vacuum in its west central part, enough in itself to impede progress forever.

But the pessimists — whether motivated by conviction or wishful thinking—were wrong, and when the fertility of western soils and suitability for grains were finally established, people from far parts of the world looked longingly. In the subsequent campaigns to attract settlers, the wheat-growing potential of homestead soil was the best of all lures.

Informed of the wheatlands available to people prepared to make homes and accept heavy work, immigrants came by the thousands. Continuing westward from Winnipeg—Gateway to the West—they fanned out to find the homestead land on which they could build and cultivate.

To those who came from peasant communities beyond the Atlantic, the promise of quarter-section farms suitable for the growing of wheat was too good to be true. Great was the relief when they reached destinations and dug anxious fingers into soil which gave reassurance of its beneficence.

Thousands of earnest and eager settlers guided tired horses or obstinate oxen and plows in half-mile furrows. The landscape changed quickly, and although mistakes and reverses were numerous enough, the undeveloped frontier became a land with a purpose.

Suddenly, it was fashionable to talk in terms of praise instead of condemnation about the West. John Macoun[2] reported boastingly in his book *Manitoba and The Great North-West* (1882) of wheat yielding fifty-five bushels to the acre, individual turnips weighing twenty-five pounds, carrots reaching a weight of eleven pounds each, cabbages growing to forty-nine pounds, and squash assuming the proportions of a rainbarrel.

A land salesman's message directed at prospective settlers in the United States urged readers: "Buy land in the Canadian West. You can leave home after Easter, sow your wheat and take in the harvest and come home with your pockets full of money in time for Thanksgiving."

Many of the stories told were tall ones, good enough to rival the best from Texas. "When you plant wheat," one promoter warned, "you must be prepared to flee immediately or become entangled and lost in the jungle of the fast-growing and heavy crop." The Texan's advice to anybody planting corn on his rich soil was to step back quickly to avoid being struck in the face by the growing cornstalk.

For many years after the passage of the Canadian Land Act,[3] wheat furnished most of the cash for reconstruction from frontier to pleasant and prospering community. It appeared about the only western resource product capable of contributing substantially to area progress. Simultaneously hard western wheat, reaching distant markets, won more international attention for the young country and gave it a new and finer stature among the nations.

Quickly, wheat became the lifeblood of half of Canada. It shared with weather the distinction of being the most popular of all subjects for conversation. Most promissory notes were dated for payment on the first day of November because farmers would have their wheat returns by that time. Baby boys received given names like Fife and Garnet and Marquis in honor of wheat varieties, and a few girls called Ruby obtained their name in the same way. Railway boxcars were designed to hold 1,000 bushels of wheat. Manufacturers and business organizations studied western crop reports and planned operations accordingly. Farms were sold for specified amounts of wheat, and governments in power aimed to hold general elections at times when wheat growers had the least cause for worry or complaint.

As a new oil field or new movie star attracts attention, so people near and far heard much and read much about Canadian wheat and its unbeatable baking qualities. Citizens knew it was their bread, if not their butter, and the best wheat in the world. Those with sentiment found added reason for pride when Seager Wheeler of Saskatchewan, and dozens of growers following him, won international championships with wheat from the still-new western soil.

There was no doubt about it! Western wheat became one of the first and best sources of the energy needed to turn the wheels of Canadian industry. Citizens, although proud of the quality of the grain and of the achievements of the growers, were slow to appreciate fully what wheat had done for both the domestic economy and the export trade.

The products of mines and oil fields managed, at times, to dominate the Canadian business scene, but as a consistent force for many years, wheat was outstanding. There were crop failures and market disappointments, but in a recent year (1966)—ninety years after the first wheat was sold from the Prairies—the volume of Canadian sales abroad exceeded anything experienced previously. Instead of diminishing, as non-renewable resources must do, wheat from western fields behaved much like the widow's unfailing oil and meal in the days of the Prophet Elijah.

"Wheat," said the *Canada Year Book*, 1965, "continues to be the major field crop in terms of gross farm value and is the major cash crop. The gross farm value of all crops in 1962 amounted to $2,118,804,000 and wheat contributed $941,436,000 or 44 p.c. of this total. In Saskatchewan alone the 1962 wheat crop was valued at $591,180,000, making up more than a quarter of the gross farm value of all Canadian field crops."

For many years wheat accounted for more than half of the food tonnage moving in international channels, and Canada was always the biggest or second biggest of the exporters. As earners of foreign exchange, the products of forest and mines have deserved praise, but taking it over the years since the opening up of the West, wheat has been far in the lead.

The *Canada Year Book* showed the value of wheat exported in 1965 at $786,804,000, with newsprint paper running second at $759,990,000, then lumber at $452,484,000, wood pulp at $405,292,000, aluminum at $302,730,000, iron ores and concentrates at $270,949,000, and crude petroleum at $233,000,000.

Upon the business life of the nation—the East as well as the West—the impact of wheat has been quite beyond easy reckoning, although agriculturists and economists have tried many times to assess its influence.

The marketing of 300,000,000 or 600,000,000 bushels of wheat has brought employment and benefit to Canadians far beyond farm fields.

Easy to see, though not easy to measure, have been the additional wages created for men in railroad service, lake and ocean shipping, elevator operation, milling, baking, banking, administration, manufacture of farm machinery and other essentials, distribution, sales, and so on. "My sales rise and fall with the farm trade in wheat," a city car dealer confessed. There seems no limit to the stimulating influence of a big western crop.

Wheat, as every grower has known from bitter experience, has not always been in triumph. Often it has been in trouble because of prairie drought, hungry grasshoppers, wet weather at harvest time, failing markets, or some other agent of disaster. The never-ending wheat stories in the news should remind Canadians of their reliance upon wheat and of the multiple problems in its production. In the House of Commons so much has been heard about wheat over the years that members came to see themselves as authorities on the subject, whether or not they could actually explain the difference between Marquis and marigolds.

The monotonously many debates about wheat farmers, wheat prices, wheat markets, and wheat ills led Hon. Ian Mackenzie[4] to pen a verse for the benefit of government colleagues:

> "The girls in spring call: 'Sweet, Sweet Sweet,'
> The tree-top birds sing: 'Tweet, Tweet Tweet,'
> The little lambs go: 'Bleat, Bleat Bleat,'
> But the damndest word I ever heard
> Is: 'Wheat, Wheat Wheat.'"

Whether the news reports are favorable or unfavorable, wheat fortunes in the three Midwestern provinces, where roughly 95 per cent of the total Canadian crop is produced, affect just about every Canadian, touching both his dinner table and his wallet. Rural and urban people alike are bread eaters, with an annual consumption of three bushels of wheat per capita. Nobody can overlook the prominence of bread in the modern diet. What the public has overlooked, too often, is that more Canadians have jobs and that people from coast to coast enjoy increased prosperity when crops and markets are favorable. Every Canadian has a stake in wheat and a debt to wheat.

CHAPTER II

༺ ☙ ༻

FROM FIELDS AFAR

༺ ❧ ༻

Wheat, the most important and most cosmopolitan of cereals grown today, has been feeding mankind for thousands of years. To a big part of the world's people it means bread, and bread means survival.

Whatever may be the objections raised against wheat as a substitute for gold and silver, the very fact it is mentioned from time to time as a medium for international currency indicates its universal acceptance and appreciation.

On the pages of world history, wheat has left impressions as plain as rabbit tracks in fresh snow. Even though those marks of time are unmistakably clear, the exact origin of bread wheat has remained in doubt. No wild wheats grew in the Western World, and North American Indians who were growing maize, beans, and tobacco when the first white men came upon the scene knew nothing about wheat.

Mesopotamia, or some other territory east of the Mediterranean, has been seen as a likely place of origin for common wheats. Certain wild grasses thought to be relatives of the wheat species have been found there, among them an emmer[5] type of wild wheat indigenous to the Syrian Mountains. It should be noted, too, that wild wheat of spelt[5] type has been discovered in Afghanistan, and several wheat-like grasses have been identified in Ethiopia. However, the particular wild form which might have been recognized as the direct ancestor of modern bread wheats has not been found and must be presumed to have disappeared.

Regardless of the wild race from which common wheat came, there is good reason to believe that domestication coincided roughly with the birth of agriculture in Mesopotamia or Egypt or both.

Recognition of the advantages of growing wheat and other food crops on cultivated ground was no doubt the main reason Neolithic nomads decided to change their ways and settle in permanent communities. Bread and sundry vegetable foods would be seen as delightful additions to diets previously restricted to meat, milk and cheese, and cultivation represented a big forward step. In addition, the adoption of permanent homes would encourage the collection of personal and artistic treasures, another step in the civilizing advance.

One of those early communities was certainly in Egypt where sediment from Nile floods enriched valley soils and created conditions favorable for cropping. Another was in Mesopotamia, believed by some scholars to have been the site of the Garden of Eden. Which of the two regions was first, nobody can say; nor does it matter very much.

Whether or not that well-favored area east of the Mediterranean was the scene of frolicking by Adam and Eve, it was a fruitful land. There, between the Euphrates and Tigris Rivers—marked by present-day Iraq— it was easy for nomads to linger and plant. Wheat and barley would respond handsomely. Because the countryside offered so many advantages for hungry tribesmen, it was frequently the scene of battle, with one or another envious race of nomadic people hoping to gain possession. The real grain-growing pioneers in that part may have been the Sumerians, who had crude hand tools for cultivation and irrigated and grew crops of wheat and barley about 6000 years ago.

Carbonized kernels of wheat, found in Egyptian tombs where they were placed to provide for the possible needs of dead Pharaohs enroute to the Spirit World, have been recognizable after some 5000 or 6000 years. Wheat growing, as the Children of Israel discovered, was an important industry in Ancient Egypt; grain grown there was one of the early items of Mediterranean commerce. It was regularly exported to Greece, Rome, and other neighboring countries.

The kernels of wheat found in Egyptian tombs and thoroughly blackened from age were objects of world-wide interest following discovery, and they inspired stories that were less than truthful. The possibility that wheat taken from the Pyramids had retained its germinating power and would grow upon planting in the twentieth century was too fantastic to warrant more than passing attention. Remarkable enough was the fact that the grains had sufficient of their original character to permit identification. Nobody should have been expected to have believed the seeds would grow after so many centuries. Yet many did think so.

When hungry Hebrews in famine-ravished Canaan of 3700 years ago heard of "corn in Egypt," they knew it meant wheat and bread. "Get you down thither and buy for us from thence that we may live and not die," Jacob said to his sons, not knowing that his lost boy, Joseph, was at the time the man in charge of all the wheat and grain resources of Egypt.

Joseph's is one of the great success stories from the Old Testament. Having been sold by jealous brothers, the boy was taken to Egypt, but instead of becoming a slave in the land of Pharaoh, Joseph won the King's favor by interpreting a royal dream and warning the sovereign thereby of seven years of crop failure and famine which would follow seven good and fruitful years. Grateful for the warning, the King elevated the young Hebrew to a position of highest authority and made him, more or less, the Chief Commissioner of an Egyptian Wheat Board, charged with buying all the surplus grain in the good years and storing it for distribution and use in the lean years.

Success ensured lasting favor, and Joseph obtained the King's permission to bring his father and brothers from Canaan, where they were facing starvation, to settle in the Land of Goshen on Egypt's east side. There, the Children of Israel did well and multiplied, which was all right until "there arose up a new king over Egypt which knew not Joseph." What followed was persecution, then the spectacular escape under the leadership of Moses, and ultimately, arrival in the Promised Land——"A land of wheat, and barley, and vines, and fig trees, and pomegranates; a land of olive oil and honey. . ."

The Old Testament contains a substantial amount of agricultural and crop history, and its many references to corn can be taken to mean wheat and barley. Adam could be considered a horticulturist. His two sons were also primary producers; Cain went in for field crops and Abel for livestock. That the world's first grain farmer murdered the first stockman has given members of Stock Growers' Associations lasting suspicions and distrust! Certainly the bloody crime did nothing to aid the many subsequent programs intended to promote agricultural unity and mixed farming. Furthermore, pursuing the growers of wheat intermittently ever since the time of Cain has been the curse imposed upon the agronomist murderer: "When thou tillest the ground it shall not henceforth yield unto thee her strength." Many times in Canadian wheat history, dried-out, hailed-out and frozen-out growers have believed they could hear Abel's blood "crying unto them from the ground."

Swiss Lake Dwellers, attracted by opportunities for good sanitation afforded when homes were built on piles above water, also cultivated wheat and barley and millet about 5000 years ago, and the Chinese planted wheat almost as long ago. The people of classical Greece and Rome used wheat as their staple food. In the fifth century B.C., during the years of Pericles, father of Athenian democracy, the seafaring merchants of Greece frequently transported wheat.

Anything as great and wonderful as wheat could not have escaped becoming enmeshed in superstition and mythology. Egypt's cultivated crops qualified for a special female deity, Isis. The Romans recognized agriculture through the Goddess Ceres, who watched benevolently over field crops, especially those of the cereal group including wheat. When Proserpina, her daughter, was kidnaped and taken away to Hades, Ceres devoted herself completely to a search for the lost child and neglected the wheat and other crops of the earth. A total crop failure resulted. Naturally, the people of Rome suffered from the famine and prayed that such a thing would not happen again. Since it was important to be on good terms with the Goddess controlling food crops, the Romans built temples for her pleasure and celebrated the Festival of Cerealia.

When Columbus made his famous voyage of discovery in 1492, wheat was being grown in every country of Europe; and it is not surprising that Spaniards lost no time in sending seed to the New World, first for planting on Caribbean Islands, and then, in 1519, on the Mexican mainland.

On what was to become Canada, French colonists were the first wheat planters. Port Royal, founded in 1604 in Nova Scotia's lovely Annapolis Valley, became the first settlement of white people in the New World since the Norsemen. Following the founding of Port Royal, de Monts and Champlain continued along the Bay of Fundy coastline and fixed upon a small island in the St. Croix River for another colony. There they planted rye. Two years later, 1606, an important group of French colonists arrived at Port Royal, and although it was late in the season—July 27—the men set about to plant the seeds of wheat, rye, turnips, and other vegetables they had brought with them.

Among the colonists at Port Royal was Louis Hébert, a friend of the redoubtable Champlain. He came as an apothecary, but later, beside the St. Lawrence River, qualified for recognition as Canada's first genuine farmer. From the time of his arrival at Port Royal, Hébert showed keen interest in experimentation with plants. He returned to France, but crossed the Atlantic again in 1617 with his wife and children and settled at Quebec. He occupied soil of his choosing and grew grains, vegetables, and fruits.

Hébert's success was an important landmark in Canadian agriculture, but it was still 180 years before the arrival of the Selkirk Settlers in the vast Northwest where they made homes and conducted planting experiments with wheat and other farm crops beside the Red River—and started the story of wheat.

CHAPTER III

❦

FIRST IN THE WEST

❦

Men of the early fur trade had a fine scorn for wheat and similar fruits of cultivated soil, a scorn like the cowboy's feeling for geraniums or the football player's interest in cricket. Their business was in wild skins, and they fancied the country as it was, without rails, without laws, without conventional marital restrictions, without much moral conscience, and without plows. Only a few of them were sufficiently interested to even try planting potatoes, turnips, and barley in garden-sized plots close to their posts.

What may be the earliest reference to wheat was recorded in the minutes of the Hudson's Bay Company, May 16, 1674: "Ordered that there be provided . . . a bushel of wheate and rye, barley and oats, or a barrell of each in casks, such sortes of garden Seeds as the Governour shall advise, a bible and common prayer booke . . ."

Where the bushel of wheat was planted—if, indeed, it was planted— is not known. But the French trader, La Corne,[6] conducted some small operations in cultivation beside his post on the Saskatchewan River, east of the present city of Prince Albert, about 1753 or 1754. He thus qualifies for the distinction of being the first planter in what is now the province of Saskatchewan. A few years later, 1780, barley and cabbages were grown at Hudson's House, about thirty miles west of where Prince Albert stands.

Peter Pond[7] must be seen as the pioneer planter inside the limits of present-day Alberta. Beside the Athabaska River, he had what Alexander Mackenzie described in 1787 as a garden as fine "as I ever saw in Canada." There was, however, no reference to wheat in the present areas of Alberta or Saskatchewan for many more years.

Notwithstanding any half-hearted efforts by traders, it was on the long, narrow river-lot farms of the Selkirk Settlers[8] — within and beside the modern city of Winnipeg—that western agriculture had its beginning.

When the Highland Scot, Miles Macdonell,[9] and his twenty-three men comprising the Selkirk "Advance Guard" arrived at the Forks of the Red and the Assiniboine Rivers on August 30, 1812, they were carrying one and one-half bushels of seed wheat, brought all the way from Scotland. They cherished a hope it would grow successfully and furnish larger quantities of both seed and grain for bread.

Halting on the east side of the Red River where the city of St. Boniface was destined to arise, the Scottish leader exchanged grudging greetings with servants of the North West Company whose Fort Gibraltar had been built on the west side of the Red River a couple of years earlier.

In a display of boldness, five days after arrival, Macdonell called his followers and a few Indian spectators together, faced the North West Company fort and used his loudest voice to read the patent which was his authority to take over the 116,000 square miles of territory. This included portions of present-day Manitoba, Saskatchewan, Minnesota and North Dakota. Having proclaimed his purpose, he ordered the firing of flintlocks, then retiring to his tent to complete the formalities opened a keg of spirits and invited the Nor'Westers to join him. It was an invitation which not even enemies could refuse.

Macdonell and his men were there to make preparations for the settlers who would be arriving shortly. Without delay, he went searching for a suitable location for building and cultivating. The spot chosen was at Point Douglas, a short distance below the confluence.

Food was scarce and the dire fact worried Macdonell. The buffalo being some distance away, the newcomers were obliged to rely upon fish taken from the rivers, and potatoes purchased at Fort Gibraltar.[10] The leader's decision was to send most of his men upstream to Pembina,[10] and keep only enough workers to dig a plot of ground to receive the bushel and a half of precious winter wheat seed, and to cut wild hay for the two cattle (called Adam and Eve) brought along from one of the Hudson's Bay posts on the route from York Factory.

Late in October, Macdonell's Advance Guard was joined by the next immigrant group—men, women and children, mainly from Ireland. Their arrival compounded the problem of finding adequate food and shelter. These newcomers had completed the long journey from their native land to the Red River in the single season. Although disappointed in finding neither homes nor fields of cultivation ready for them, they took some comfort in the knowledge that a bushel and a half of winter wheat had been planted.

When spring came in 1813, settlers returned from Pembina to Point

Douglas to build homes, cultivate, do some further planting, and watch the growth on the plot of wheat. Peter Fidler came down from Brandon House and used his surveyor's knowledge to lay out the long, narrow river-lot farms—about one hundred acres in each—for which the settlers were expected to pay at the rate of five shillings per acre. Macdonell and his people soon discovered that the new land harbored dozens of forces capable of bringing ruin to crops of wheat. The bushel and one-half of winter wheat planted in the autumn amounted to nothing. Starting late in the season, the plants were unable to survive the winter. Another sack of wheat obtained for spring planting did no better, leading Macdonell, in the month of July, to admit total wheat failure.

But the failure was not really complete because, as told by Alexander Ross,[11] Red River historian and author of *Red River Settlement,* one of the new farmers obtained an almost unbelievable yield, 12½ bushels of wheat from 4 quarts planted. In other words, the recovery of 750 pounds came from 7½ pounds of seed, an increase of exactly a hundredfold. It showed that by exercising special care and skill, one grower was able to reap a big return on his small patch of broken ground when others had crop failures.

But Macdonell called it a year of failure, and so it must be seen. Most people in the community found it difficult to muster much optimism for plantings in the next year, 1814. And, sure enough, there was further failure. The wheat started well, but a late summer frost ruined it for anything except cattle fodder. The only encouragement came from potatoes and turnips which yielded well and helped to relieve the shortage of food.

With new seed difficult to obtain, the settlers might have considered the time proper to abandon all thought of growing wheat, but for the 1815 season they had fresh seed brought from the Old Country; and hopefully they placed it in the soil.

The community was still without farm implements more imposing than spades and hand hoes, with the result that cultivated plots had not been expanded by much. Again settlers watched crop progress assiduously and found reason for rejoicing in the early growth of foliage, but in June the peace of the Valley was rudely broken by the arrival of a band of warlike men—Nor'Westers and their Métis[12] supporters, mounted, armed, and belligerent. Their resentment toward settlement or anything in conflict with the fur trade had been mounting steadily. A farming community situated at the junction of the two rivers, of all places, looked like a threat to their vital trade communications, and to show their anger they rattled their guns, trampled the crop, set fire to buildings, and took Miles Macdonell a prisoner. Alarmed by this outburst, some of the settlers accepted the offer of transportation in North West Company canoes to find new homes in Upper Canada, while the others—except for a John McLeod and three friends—abandoned their holdings and departed by canoe to seek safety at the north end of Lake Winnipeg.

With a double portion of Scottish stubbornness, McLeod and his three friends took shelter in one of the log houses, drew the colony's three-pounder cannon into an advantageous position, cut logging chains into short lengths for use as cannon shot, and waited for an attack. They did not have long to wait. The cannon's roar rivaled the Rupert's Land thunder and served to frighten more of the half-breeds than it killed. The assailants withdrew, glad to leave McLeod alone. Then, with the Point Douglas area pretty well to themselves, the four men watched the damaged crops recover.

In the meantime, Colin Robertson,[18] under instructions from Lord Selkirk, arrived with a party of men capable of putting up a good fight on the settlers' behalf. Robertson continued northward to assure the settlers, if they would come back, of protection from hostile enemies. The refugees did return. To greet them was a crop of ripening wheat and barley, the first they had experienced. It helped to reduce the multiple anxieties, and when the new Governor, Robert Semple, arrived in November, one of his first acts was to make an assessment of the number of people to be fed and the available resources with which to feed them. The human population stood at 120 and the available grain totaled 400 bushels of wheat and 200 bushels of barley. Semple's plan called for keeping back 40 bushels for the 1816 planting, leaving 560 bushels for winter rations, about 235 pounds per person.

Spring brought fresh hope—as spring does always—and the forty bushels of seed grain were carefully spread broadcast on a score or more of small fields. The crop started well enough, but how it grew later in the season none of the Selkirk people ever knew. It was the year of the great tragedy, the year of the bloody clash between Governor Semple's men and Cuthbert Grant's predominantly half-breed group which left the Governor and twenty of his followers dead on the field at Seven Oaks.[14] It happened on June 19, and again, saddened and distraught settlers fled northward to find safety and be far removed from those unhappy Red River surroundings. At harvest time, the Nor'Westers were still occupying Fort Douglas— the fortification built at the Point bearing the same name—and no crop was recovered.

Refugee settlers felt the depth of despair and showed no desire to return to Red River, but early in the new year (1817) soldiers sent from the East by Lord Selkirk arrived and recaptured Fort Douglas. News that the settlement was again in friendly hands was dispatched to the frustrated settlers, also a plea to come back to their riverside homes. Fearfully and reluctantly, they returned in time to plant what little wheat and other seed they could gather together, hoping, as always, for the best. But Nature's mood was no better. The crop of 1817 became the victim of early frost. For the fourth time in five plantings, the settlers harvested less wheat than they invested in the soil.

The Nor'Westers giggled with satisfaction; a few more Selkirk people gave up the struggle and went elsewhere; but others, with the spirit of John McLeod, prepared for the next season's planting of wheat and barley and potatoes.

CHAPTER IV

THE PLAGUE OF LOCUSTS

The soil and climate of Rupert's Land displayed some ugly moods during the first five Selkirk years which did nothing to help in the building of local confidence. Perhaps the next five years would be better; but they were not better. Instead of being more kindly toward the new tillers of the soil, Nature seemed to find delight in co-operating with the enemies of settlement by making it easier for men to say: "The traders were right. Cultivation will never be a success in these inhospitable parts."

The next destructive force rode in on wild wings. It was even more damaging than a summer frost because all forms of foliage as well as grains were lost. Grasshoppers came without warning, were thorough and merciless, and left practically no wheat or other green thing.

The crop of 1818 started well enough, and then, suddenly, on a late July afternoon when barley was beginning to fill and wheat was coming into head, westerly winds brought grasshoppers in clouds which, according to Alexander Ross, "darkened the air and fell like a heavy shower of snow upon the devoted colony. . . . Next morning when the people arose it was not to gladness but to sorrow; all their hopes were in a moment blighted. Crops, gardens and every green herb in the settlement had perished, with the exception of a few ears of barley, half ripe, gleaned in the women's aprons. This sudden and unexpected disaster was more than they could bear. The unfortunate immigrants, looking up toward heaven, wept."

With the approach of winter and another threat of famine, settlers moved again to Pembina where they would be closer to buffalo herds and more likely to find rations of wild meat.

The grasshopper attacker was probably the Rocky Mountain locust, a species capable of long flights of migration and extreme destructiveness. Settlers in the western States knew the pest well and feared it bitterly, but after the western plains were developed this particular species made fewer and fewer appearances and practically disappeared from the region.

For planting in the spring of 1819 there was only the small amount of seed gathered by painstaking mothers and wives who virtually combed the fields for individual cereal heads missed by the hoppers. But it did not matter about the acreage because the crop was again eaten by the ravenous insects. The hoppers were still there, and if anything in larger numbers, "not by a new flight of the pestilence of last year," as Ross explained, "but still worse, by the countless swarms produced in the ground itself. . . . It is impossible to describe adequately, the desolation thus caused. Every vegetable substance was either eaten up or stripped to the bare stalk; the leaves of the bushes and the bark of the trees shared the same fate. The grain vanished as fast as it appeared above ground, leaving no hope either of seed to the sower or bread to the eater . . . the decomposition of [grasshopper] bodies when dead was still more offensive than their presence when alive."

Destruction was so complete that the Red River women searching for occasional heads of grain containing seed found nothing. If there was to be another planting, it would have to be with imported seed, and importation was not a simple matter; the nearest supply was believed to be far away in Wisconsin. With admirable determination to survive the many enemies of cropping, settlers organized to send a deputation of their men on the long and uninviting winter journey to Prairie du Chien, in the southern part of that state. Some of the men had no idea where Wisconsin was located, but they started on their way to find seed wheat. Much of their travel was on snowshoes. After three months of hardships on winter trails and over country without trails, the men were able to make important purchases. They bought 250 bushels of wheat at ten shillings per bushel.

When the transaction was finished, rapidly melting snow had caused rivers to run high. Conditions suited the Selkirk men, for they were then able to construct rafts and flat-bottomed boats on which to convey their precious cargo back to Point Douglas. The floating structures loaded with wheat were maneuvred upstream on the Mississippi River and into the Minnesota River. Their difficult course took them through Big Stone Lake, and finally on the Red River to their destination at Point Douglas.

It was June before the Prairie du Chien wheat was delivered to the settlers, and there was some hesitation in planting at the late date. Moreover, the high cost of purchasing and delivering the 250 bushels—more than a thousand pounds in total—was well noted. Fortunately for the settlers, however, the Selkirk Estate magnanimously agreed to pay the big bill.

Having made up their minds to plant wheat even in June, the Red River farmers lost no time in getting the seed into the ground. To their anxiety, the grasshopper threat was still present, and for a time it appeared that the crop would be destroyed for the third successive year. But, for reasons historian Ross is unable to explain, the hoppers disappeared. Then, in spite of the late planting and the early-season work of grass-hoppers, the settlers obtained enough wheat for the next year's seed—just enough, with practically nothing over for gristing.

The crop of 1821 was better but still not big enough to eliminate the necessity of some settlers going again to winter at Pembina where they could be reasonably sure of buffalo meat rations. For those who remained at Point Douglas, it was a bad winter. Immigrant arrivals meant more mouths to feed, and near-famine conditions prevailed. Ross tells of one hungry newcomer from Switzerland exchanging his valuable silver watch for eight gallons of wheat for bread purposes.

If there was anything more precious than silver at that time, it was wheat. A new Governor, Alexander McDonell, even adopted wheat for use in some of his accounting. Known as the Grasshopper Governor, this one failed to win community confidence and was remembered for revelry at Fort Douglas rather than for assistance brought to the settlers. Anyway, when rum or some other commodity from the Governor's stores was dispensed, instead of counting sales to the various customers by the usual pen-and-ink entries, McDonell would authorize the filling of the heel of a bottle with wheat and placing it on a cask. This was called the Hourglass and as each flagon was drawn to fill an order, a grain of wheat was removed and set aside as a charge against the purchaser. When the party ended, the grains were counted and consumers could see exactly how many times they had visited the bar. Each customer was then expected to make settlement in some more acceptable currency.

As Ross has told it: "From time to time the great man at the head of the table would display his moderation by calling out to his butler: 'Bob, how stands the hourglass?' 'High, your honour, high!' was the general reply, as much as to say, they had drunk but little yet."

There was reason to believe the grasshopper disappearance was not really complete. Probably the parasites were at least partly responsible for food shortages of 1821, serious indeed. Although Alexander Ross seemed to think the destructive insects had vanished, George Simpson, writing to Andrew Colville on September 8, 1821, (from Champlain Society, Minutes of Council of Northern Department, 1821-31) expressed a totally different opinion: "The Grasshopper, I am extremely sorry to say, continues its destructive influence; the crops have been seriously injured and in many parts wholly destroyed, yet with care and economy there will be no danger of starvation during the winter, indeed at Red River, if people have but strength and common industry and exertion they may always live well; the plains afford an inexhaustible stock of animal food and if even the Buffalo disappointed them, which is next to impossible, with a few nets any number of people may be maintained by the Lake near the mouth of the River. I cannot, however, recommend your sending any more settlers from Europe, far less from Canada until we see if the Grasshopper disappears; many are of the opinion that this will be their last season, as they no sooner take wing, than they migrate in large swarms; if this should be realized, it would be a most fortunate circumstance and dispel the gloom which seems to hang over the truly unfortunate colony."

Nobody expected George Simpson, whose heart was in the fur trade, to be overly enthusiastic about farming operations. As a matter of duty, he could bring himself to provide assistance for the settlers, but his complete dedication to their needs could be questioned. In spite of grasshoppers and all the other forces working against progress, however, some headway could be noted. As originals among the settlers looked back upon ten years at Red River, a census showed total annual plantings reached 235 bushels of wheat, 142 bushels of barley, 570 bushels of potatoes, and a few bushels of Indian corn and peas. It is significant that the bushel plantings of potatoes were still far above those of wheat. Wheat could not yet be said to have passed the experimental stage. Of the ten growing seasons, not more than two could be called fruitful for the grain.

Any way one looked at the Red River effort, it was still experimental agriculture and nobody could be confident of a future for farming. And if any observer thought he had seen all the varieties of trouble for growers held in Nature's bag of tricks, he was due for some surprises. There were still some heartbreaking experiences for those who hoped to grow wheat in the fur country.

CHAPTER V

❦

MORE CROP LOSSES

❦

Throughout prairie history, an occasional big crop of wheat has been enough to dull the memory of bad years and fill farmers with new determination to stay on the land. Seager Wheeler[15] of wheat championship fame recalled drought years around Moose Jaw in 1884, 1885, 1886, and 1887, followed by the big crop of 1888 which squashed all thought of giving up. Homesteaders dried out in 1912, 1913, and 1914 obtained a bumper crop in 1915 and proclaimed intention to stay and grow wheat. So it was in 1824—the twelfth year for planting in the Red River Settlement—growth response brought both surprise and reassurance to nearly everybody.

Alexander Ross reported yields as high as sixty-eight bushels of wheat per acre on ground cultivated with a hand hoe and forty-four bushels per acre on plowed land. It was the first year a plow had been used, and although all yields were good, some people saw clear indication of the hoe's superiority over any newfangled gadget hauled by horses or oxen.

It was reassuring to know that Red River soil and climate could combine to produce such abundance, but the skeptic warned that Nature, in her trickery, was just lulling the settlers into a sense of false security, to hold them for more years of punishment. Sure enough, the varied resources of natural obstinacy were demonstrated again; 1825 was the year of mice; 1826, the year of the flood.

Birds—mainly passenger pigeons—constituted a constant threat which settlers came to accept as a man might accept chronic rheumatism. Flying in flocks of millions, these particular pigeons, although destined to total extinction in less than a hundred years, were quite capable of inflicting severe crop damage.

As Alexander Ross recorded it: "Every spring we may observe myriads of blackbirds and wild pigeons pass the colony in their migrations to the

North, and return again on their way to the South, during the time of harvest, and that in such clouds as to threaten the little patches of grain with total destruction, more particularly in years when there are no berries. On these occasions, bird nets, guns and scarecrows are all in active operation, and also men, women and children going constantly about their little parterres, from morning till night, and yet all often proves ineffectual to repel the formidable enemy. Fortunately, however, this evil is diminishing every year."

It was easy enough to understand the bird migrations, but whence came the mice in that year of 1825? Their appearance late in the season had some of the suddenness which characterized the coming of grasshoppers a few years before. As if they had come out of the sky, the mice were everywhere, in the houses, in the storage quarters, and in the fields. After harvest, they concentrated upon grain in stacks. Comments made by eyewitnesses suggested that they left very little wheat or other grain for human consumption. Even the stubble was chewed to bits.

Perhaps the plague of mice, "another great calamity," would have continued into the next year and the next had not Nature provided another form of violence in 1826—floods, sufficient to drive every living thing from the valley lands.

When Selkirk people spoke in reverent awe about "The Flood," they referred to either the biblical flood or the local disaster of 1826, which in crest level was higher than any Red River flood known since that time.

The high water of 1826, according to water marks determined by Sir Sandford Fleming, touched 36.75 feet City Datum[16] and was thus considerably above the 30.3 foot peak in the memorable flood of 1950.

Heavy rains fell in the autumn of 1825 with the following winter unusually long and severe. Snow was said to have accumulated to five feet in the woods. Moreover, the mild weather of spring came late and completed the perfect combination of circumstances for the production of a flood.

The river breakup, signaled by the roar of huge, cascading blocks of ice, came during the first week of May. Rain and snow accompanied the breakup to add to the weight of water in the Red River channel. The river level came up nine feet in the single day, May 2, enough to overflow the channel banks and send settlers into wild confusion. People attempted to rescue cattle and some personal belongings before they took flight to dry ground well back from the river.

Some settlers who thought they were safe found floodwater entering their homes during the night and were obliged to take refuge on the rooftops. Neighbors in boats had to rescue them the following morning. Two men who chose the top of a haystack as a place to sleep in safety awakened in the morning to find their haystack bed was floating freely, well on its way to Lake Winnipeg. Company boats were kept busy making rescues and bringing relief to stranded people. Miraculously, only one life was lost as a result of the flood.

Anything which would float was carried away by the cruel current. Settlers watched in utter helplessness as their belongings were swept toward the lake. The level continued to rise until May 21, when hardly a house remained in the riverside colony. According to a Fort Garry journal kept by Francis Heron, an employee of the Hudson's Bay Company, forty-seven houses were carried away in the space of half an hour on May 5.

For the time being at least, all thought of planting wheat was abandoned. Heron, on May 31, after the water had receded considerably, concluded that any planting on the cultivated land at the settlement during the season was most unlikely. With warm days the familiar urge to be planting, grew. Some of the settlers, Heron noted, while still camping far back from the river, "commenced breaking up new ground where such is to be found dry, in which they plant small quantities of wheat, to prevent its becoming once more extinct in the settlement."

By late June the settlers had moved back to their own land and valiantly planted what small amounts of barley and potatoes they had managed to save. Being still wet, the gumbo mud made seeding extremely difficult, but when seed was successfully covered, it sprouted rapidly and gave surprisingly good growth.

The setback brought discouragement, described by George Simpson when he wrote to his Company colleagues in London on June 14, 1826: "A calamity of the most unforeseen nature presented itself, one which I conceive to be a death-blow to the colony; the immediate distress, occasioned thereby is beyond description, and the consequences threatening the lives of its wretched inhabitants. This evil, to which all the others that this truly unfortunate colony has been from time to time visited, put together, bear no comparison, was occasioned by the overflowing of the Red and Assiniboine rivers on the breaking up of the ice to such an extent as to give the whole country, as far as the eye could carry, the appearance of a lake, with the exception of a few elevated spots at the distance of several miles from each other, whither the settlers retreated to save their lives, and such of their property as could be transported thither . . . in short, such a scene of misery has been rarely witnessed and almost baffles description."

Seed wheat priced at two shillings a bushel before the flood commanded fifteen shillings after it. That anybody would be interested in purchasing seed at such late date seems strange, but the settlers evidently could not get away entirely from the compulsion to plant. Actually, some of the late plantings proved quite successful. Potatoes and barley planted as late as June 20 matured to give a fair return. Even patches of wheat matured sufficiently to return seed and a little more.

The flood was one more test in a long series. The decision to return to clean up and build again at Red River took almost superhuman courage. Not all the people who fled from the flood were prepared to face the new task. The De Meurons and some others admitted to having had enough, and on June 24 departed for some undetermined destination in the United States. However, a stubborn element, as Ross has explained, refused to give up.

"The Scotch settlers," he wrote, "meanwhile, not so easily chilled by disappointments, promptly decided on the course they would take: without a moment's hesitation, or loss of time, they resumed their work on their cheerless farms, which were then bare and naked as on the first day they came to the country. This was the fourth time the Scotch settlers had commenced the world anew in Red River, all the fruits of their labours having disappeared, like the morning dew."

It is doubtful if many other settlers in the long history of agriculture faced such persistent and grueling tests as those in the Selkirk colony endured, and remained to farm. Somewhere in this people was an inexhaustible store of faith that better times lay ahead. George Simpson was quite wrong in supposing the flood disaster would prove to be a "death-blow" to the colony. The settlers were proved right in their premonition. Those better times with good crops of wheat and barley were not to be realized quickly, but they were to come.

CHAPTER VI

❧

BETTER TIMES

❧

For those stubborn spirits who stayed to challenge all the varied obstacles to the growing of wheat at Red River, the first fifteen years were the worst. Recovery from flood devastation was rapid enough to have surprised even a man of such fiber as John McLeod. Silt from the turbid floodwater refreshed the fertility of the valley soils and the favorable year of 1827 seemed to mark the beginning of better times. The departure of those immigrants who would surrender to frontier adversity left the colony with none but robust types, the best possible seed stock for a pioneer farming community. By 1830, the settlement was pretty well re-established.

Gradually, settlers obtained equipment and learned to use it. Even though the wheatland prepared by means of the hand hoe had far out-yielded the plowed ground in 1824—first year for the new implement in the settlement—the plow was winning approval. To make the first Red River plow, materials had to be imported through Hudson's Bay, at costs which made it seem almost prohibitive—a shilling per pound for the iron and an additional three pence per pound for freight. Costs, however, had been reduced, and settlers began to see plows as necessities rather than luxuries, for by no other means could cultivated acreage be expanded significantly. To pull the new walking plow inventions—the West's first advance toward mechanization of agriculture—a man could obtain ponies from the Indians or oxen reared in the settlement. Either were quite acceptable.

Those first plows, hammered out in Red River smithies, were crude implements and never acquired polished surfaces which would remain clear in the heavy clay soils. In spite of all shortcomings, the new plows produced revolutionary changes in local methods. Fall plowing became standard Red River practice. Simultaneously, settlers began fashioning homemade harrows for leveling and breaking down the gumbo sod. It was all greatly different from the methods of the first years, a mere decade or two before.

Just about every adult could comprehend the operation of a plow or harrow, but a windmill, that much envied generator of power, was quite a different matter. The first one at Red River proved to be too much for local ingenuity. In the earliest years, wheat intended for flour was ground by means of the primitive device called a "quern," consisting, essentially, of two flat stones having grinding surfaces, one placed above the other. The lower or "nether" stone was stationary, the upper one free to be rotated by hand as grain was fed into the space between. Such grinding by hand methods was, naturally, slow and tedious. The possibility of employing a waterwheel or windmill was hopefully considered.

The first windmill was set up for operation about 1825. It is believed that this was the mill sent out by Lord Selkirk some ten years earlier and returned to England when nobody was able to assemble it for service. But when shipped across the Atlantic, westward, on the second occasion, it was placed in working order by a Scottish millwright, sent out expressly for the purpose by Lord Selkirk's executors. All things considered, it stood as a very expensive piece of equipment, with total costs not less than £1,500. Then, soon after being set in working order, it was sold to a Mr. Logan in whose ownership it did long service in grinding Red River wheat.

Times were changing. Needed was an experimental farm or something of the kind where new methods could be demonstrated and where settlers might be spared the costliness of individual trial-and-error operations. The need had not been overlooked, even before Lord Selkirk's death in 1820, but it was easier to talk about such an institution than to organize it and set it in motion. On three occasions, however, the Hudson's Bay Company officials authorized experimental farms. The intentions were good, but none of the farms was particularly successful except in entertainment value.

The first experimental farm, the Hayfield Farm, was started, following Lord Selkirk's instructions, in 1821 and was elaborate enough in its conception. Unfortunately, plans were not carried through. As a dairy farm, it had just about everything required except dairy cows. And the fine house, built at a cost of £600, brought more ridicule than admiration.

As an experimental institution, the Hayfield Farm had to be judged a failure, but the authorities were game to try again. As reported by Robert Campbell, the second experimental farm, started in 1831, was beside the Assiniboine River, three or four miles back from the Fort. High hopes were held for it. Not only would it serve as a public demonstration of what could be accomplished by employing proper methods, but it would be an important source of food supplies of all kinds. Chief Factor McMillan was to be in charge and Robert Campbell, assistant.

After taking up residence in a tent on the new farm in 1831, Campbell had as many as forty men working under his direction, building, plowing, haying, and preparing generally for the forthcoming seeding season.

Farm equipment, such as plows, seed drills, harrows, axes, and milk pails, all of the most approved kind, was introduced. Milk cows were selected and bought for the breeding herd. The biggest attraction for the onlookers was the imported stallion, Fireaway. Brought from England at a cost of £300, the great horse—presumably of the Hackney breed—made the long journey by sailing vessel to York Factory and by York boat the rest of the way, without mishap. At once, Fireaway was Red River's finest showpiece. Even people of the native races came long distances to gaze upon him. Moreover, the horse crossed successfully with Indian mares, producing the best buffalo runners and best farm horses the frontier had known. Fireaway seemed to be the best justification for any of the experimental farm efforts.

The second experimental farm, like the first, had a short life. Governor George Simpson blamed the settlers for failure to appreciate its possible value. "Red River," said he, "is like a Libyan tiger; the more we try to tame it, the more savage it becomes." Simpson was accusing the settlers of making the country appear like a tiger, but all the fault was not with them.

After a few years, the Company embarked upon a third experimental farm, probably the most ambitious undertaking of all. This one, started in 1838, was north of the mouth of the Assiniboine. Captain George Marcus Carey from London was engaged to run it. Twenty acres of land were prepared for crop in the first year. It was an impressive beginning. The plan called for a flock of 300 sheep and a shepherd from the Scottish Highlands to provide the care. Again, the experimental farm effort, intended to reduce the risks and losses for individual farmers, won only the faintest praise and failed to survive for more than a short time.

Having weathered the storms in production, the settlers were faced next with worries in marketing. As long as Red River people were able to consume all they grew, they had no marketing problem. When production began to exceed local needs, there were the first clear shrieks of alarm about distribution and prices. To counter the growers' complaints about prices were consumers' protests about poor quality. It was exactly what might have been expected in the evolution of a trade in food commodities. Novice farmers were unfamiliar with the dangers and unable to enlist all the safeguards against produce deterioration; and consumers could not be expected to pay generously for farm goods they could not eat.

In his position as Company Governor, George Simpson tried to be helpful. As an inducement to the settlers, he bought from them all the supplies needed at the trading posts. The result was increased production, as intended, but with the old law of supply and demand exerting its influence, prices dropped substantially. Flour prices fell from sixteen shillings per hundredweight to eleven shillings, six pence; butter dropped from one shilling per pound to seven pence and cheese from six pence per pound to four pence.

The wailing occasioned by shrinking prices was no louder than the complaints from consumers who found the flour to be moldy and "altogether of so very bad quality as to be only fit to poison pigs."[17]

The idea of producing in a way to preserve the natural quality of farm goods had not occurred to the colonists. Even the Company officials seemed to have overlooked it. Ross reported that in the entire community there was no mill capable of removing smut, mouse contamination, and other foreign matter from grain. Facilities for threshing were primitive, with most of the work being done on ice floors where the grain was bound to pick up moisture. "Little wonder," Ross observed, "if the flour turned out to be of very bad quality, heated, sour and even rotten."

It was George Simpson's reasoning that the Company could to advantage store and mill the wheat. Thus, the Company, instead of the farmers, would have control over the many factors related to the ultimate quality of the flour. Accordingly, it was announced that Simpson's men would, henceforward, buy grain only, paying three shillings, six pence per bushel for wheat. Between 8,000 and 10,000 bushels were purchased in the first autumn and placed in Company storage. The new policy was fine in principle, but it carried no guarantee that the Company would be more successful than the farmers in protecting the stored grain against contamination and spoiling.

No system of grading existed, and a bushel of tough or damp wheat was taken in the same way and at the same price as a bushel of dry wheat. Some of the grain purchased was evidently very bad with smut. Anyway, the Company purchases were all dumped together where they shared storage space with large quantities of dried buffalo meat. With mice moving back and forth, enjoying complete freedom, the unappetizing grain, bearing traces of moisture, mice, meat, and smut, brought credit to nobody. Flour from this mass of impurities was shipped to distant trading posts, but there is no proof that anybody ate it willingly.

Growers in the new land had to learn everything about wheat by the costly expedient of experience. The mistakes were numerous enough; but from the lessons came more grain, better grain and better flour, altogether more in keeping with the inherent goodness of the new soil.

The census of 1849 showed the colony's total cultivation at 6,392 acres, enough to meet all needs. No longer were reports about poor flour being heard. Production was still for home consumption in the colony and at the trading posts to the west. The idea of shipping wheat or other food staples abroad was, as yet, nothing more than a dream.

CHAPTER VII

IN THE GRIP OF CONTROVERSY

Superstition and prejudice die slowly and for more than half a century after the Selkirk Settlers broke the first sod, controversy about the value of the Northwest for settlement and wheat was unending, like the flow of water in the Red River. Indeed, the spirited debate, unhampered by the pursuit of Confederation in the East, made one of the most entertaining and ridiculous chapters in the history of the West.

Men of the fur trade loved Rupert's Land just as it was, primitive, perilous, and lawless, and entrenched themselves against development. Unabashed, they offered their opinions loudly. More restrained were the voices calling for change. All might have gone unnoticed had it not been for murmurs about the possibility of the Northwest being annexed by the United States. The Imperial Government at once showed concern. American financiers, by their interest in purchasing Rupert's Land from the Hudson's Bay Company, led the Britishers to inquire if they might have overlooked something of importance in the vast and undeveloped area.

To most people in the East and overseas, the Northwest remained a land of mystery, barrenness, and bad weather. Nobody challenged the opinion of British historian, Sir Archibald Alison,[18] that "seven-eighths of British North America are doomed to eternal sterility." It was exactly what men of the fur trade wanted to hear.

Fortunately, some people occupying high places in the Imperial Government were not ready to accept such gloomy pronouncements. The Northwest, they reasoned, might be capable of yielding something better than buffalo robes and beaver skins. With a fresh demand for information, a special committee was named, and early in 1857 it was sitting in London to hear expert evidence.

One of the first witnesses called was Col. John Henry Lefroy[19] who had traveled extensively in the fur country, and his testimony was forceful. A large part of the region, he said, is "almost entirely denuded of soil." Moreover, frosts "are so intense that over a very large portion the soil is permanently frozen. The seasons are so short and so uncertain that crops are likely to be cut off." Conceding that some soil along the Saskatchewan River might lend itself to cultivation, Lefroy said that wheat had been tried at Cumberland House. As for oats, he had never heard of them being tested.

Among the witnesses to follow was George Simpson, small of stature but dynamic, the Scot who had been in Company service for thirty-seven years. For most of that long period, Simpson was the Governor. Never one to hide his opinions or authority, he spoke boldly, said he did not consider any part of the Hudson's Bay Company territory suitable for settlement. Asked if he would include Red River districts in that category of un-suitability, he replied quite emphatically: "Yes."

Invited to state reasons for such an opinion, Sir George replied: "On account of the poverty of the soil"—an error in judgment which should have haunted its author. He had one reservation: the banks of the rivers might produce very fair crops of wheat, but these crops, he hastened to add, "are frequently destroyed by early frost. . . . We have been under the necessity of importing grain from the United States and Canada for the support of the establishment."

He had more to say about frosts, plagues of grasshoppers and the occurrence of floods capable of driving settlers from homes and farms. Alluding, no doubt, to the terrible flood of 1826, he mentioned paddling "over the roofs of some of the homes in my canoe."

This was the testimony of a man with the experience of nearly forty years in the country. Having traveled the streams by canoe and the land by horse and saddle, he could say nothing encouraging about agricultural prospects at Red River and the country beyond. If land occupation were extended, settlers would not be self-supporting, he insisted. Then he repeated what he regarded as the principal reason: "The poverty of the soil."

It should not have gone unnoticed that Simpson had, indeed, tried to assist the settlers at Red River, but the years had done nothing to shake him from his pessimism or convince him that cultivation should ever supersede the fur trade.

"You are here to tell us that the country is very barren and could not support a population," a member of the committee remarked impatiently. Simpson was already on record on that point: "A population thinly scattered along the banks of the river might support themselves," he said, "but a dense population could not live in that country; the country could not afford the means of subsistence."

There were other witnesses, and the evidence became distressingly contradictory. Members of the parliamentary committee felt obliged to look elsewhere for unprejudiced answers to their questions. Their next move was one of extreme importance. Wisely, they decided upon a scientific appraisal of Rupert's Land, and just five weeks after George Simpson appeared before the enquiring body, the committee chairman sent written instructions to Captain John Palliser[20] to explore "that portion of British North America which lies between the northern branch of the River Saskatchewan and the frontier of the United States, and between the Red River and the Rocky Mountains."

On July 20, 1857, Palliser and his party of qualified assistants left Fort Garry, marking the beginning of three seasons of intensive study. As they pursued a zig-zag course westward and northwestward, digging holes here and there to examine soil, members of the party saw where potatoes had been grown at Fort Ellice, where wheat had been grown at Fort Qu'Appelle and where grains had been tried without success at Fort Carlton. Later, at Fort Edmonton, they saw where some home-grown wheat had been ground into "tolerable flour."

What they saw in native vegetation, however, was not all lush and verdant. It is possible that Palliser's years on the Prairies were drier than normal. In any case, he noted the marks of extremely dry conditions: "The sage and the cactus abound and the whole of the scanty vegetation bespeaks an arid climate." It was the sparse growth on much of the plains that led him to define the now-familiar Palliser Triangle; an extension of it was called the Great American Desert.

Palliser was cautious—as scientists should be. He reported favorably about the park belt, unfavorably about the plains. "The capabilities of this country and its climate for the success of the cereals," he said in his report, "have hardly been sufficiently tested. But I have seen first rate specimens of barley and oats grown at many of the forts. Wheat has not been so successful but I am hardly prepared to say that this was because of the unfitness of the climate to produce it. I have reason to believe that the seed has been bad and the cultivation neglected, and the spots chosen not of a suitable aspect. I have not only seen excellent wheat but also Indian corn ripening on Mr. Pratt's farm at the Qu'Appelle Lakes in 1857."

Valuable as Palliser's report was to prove, it did little to settle the arguments of the time about the best way to deal with the new country.

Henry Y. Hind,[20] as a servant of the Government of the Province of Canada, embarked upon a study of the Prairies in the same year as Palliser, and although his survey was less extensive, he found reason for optimism about the area.

John A. Macdonald, as Prime Minister of the new Dominion of Canada, favored acquisition of the West as a matter of expediency. As far as he was concerned, the net value of the new country was still in doubt, as one of his letters indicated clearly: "I would be quite willing, personally, to leave that whole country a wilderness for the next half century, but I fear if Englishmen do not go there, Yankees will."

Eastern people were thoroughly confused. There were many who agreed that the country should remain with the Hudson's Bay Company. But in spite of those who could not see much of value in the West, the British Government began to urge negotiations for the purchase of Rupert's Land. Late in 1869, more than two years after Confederation, Canada bought the territorial rights for what is now half a nation, paying $1,500,000 plus a section and three-quarters of land in every township surveyed, and certain areas close to Company trading posts. It was the biggest real estate deal in Canadian history and the most important.

But before consummation of the new purchase, there was insurrection at Red River. It was opposition to the annexation, as it was being carried out, and Louis Riel[21] and his followers gave the Government of Canada some genuine cause for worry. In due course, the resistance was removed, however, and on July 15, 1870, three years after Confederation, the West was finally transferred to Dominion of Canada authority and the ocean-to-ocean concept of the nation-builders like Sir John A. Macdonald was assured.

But at that date and even later, the pessimists were far from being silenced. "The Canadian Pacific," wrote an editor of *London Truth,* Sept. 1, 1881, "if it is ever finished, will run through a country about as forbidding as any on earth. British Columbia is not worth keeping. It should never have been inhabited at all. It will never pay a red cent of interest on the money that must be sunk in it. In Manitoba, those who are not frozen to death are maimed for life by frostbites. . . ."

For the Confederation events of 1867, people in the West had practically no concern and no interest. They were complete outsiders to the plan and gave it only the attention they might have given any foreign news. Likewise, Easterners had nothing but indifference for the West where furs produced a relatively small return, and farming was still confined to the river-lot farms along the Red and the Assiniboine. Even the purchase of Rupert's Land and the creation in 1870 of the province of Manitoba failed to awaken more than the slightest awareness—until it was discovered, suddenly, that the "ugly duckling" was displaying some new "feathers," that western soil, despite all the unflattering remarks made about it, possessed unrecognized resources for wheat growing. The first convincing demonstrations came dramatically in the mid-seventies, when Manitoba was six years old.

❧❧❧

Chapter VIII

PRELUDE TO 1876

❧❧❧

It was never easy to see good in the work of grasshoppers, but when they paid one of their recurring visits, wreaking devastation and completely eliminating the kinds of wheat grown previously, they were effectively clearing the way for a new and better variety. Although nobody could have sensed it at the time, the insects were preparing the ground for a new economic order in the West. As that particular grasshopper visitation of the seventies was to appear in the light of history, it has to be seen as a blessing in disguise.

At the moment Canadians of four eastern provinces were celebrating Confederation, the hated hoppers were moving again upon Red River. They came to stay around for some years. The insects were moderately bad in 1867 and numerous enough in the next year to totally destroy crops, leaving no wheat either for seed or flour. Even the dead hoppers beside the walls of Fort Garry were thick enough to be offensive, and people raked them into piles and carted them away. Farmers tried feeding them to pigs, but the swine showed no appetite for such fare. Other citizens resorted to burning the dead things, in the hope of ending the evil smell of the rotting remains.

The colony, bigger now, faced threat of famine, but an appeal for help brought relief from Canada's eastern provinces, the United States and Britain. Recognizing an emergency, the Council of Assiniboia voted £600 for the purchase of new seed in the United States, also £500 for flour.

Since there were no insecticides and no known means of control, the hoppers reproduced to the limit of their capacity and were only a little less of a menace in 1869 and in the next five or six years. In 1875, seed exhausted again, human patience was tested as on many previous occasions. However, determination to triumph with wheat persisted with all the tenacity of an ardent lover. Courageously, settlers backed a committee of their members for a winter journey southward, far enough to find wheat for planting—any kind of wheat. With travel by means of sleighs and ox-teams, the undertaking was, inevitably, one of hardship. However, the men were robust and carried out their purpose and returned in time for seeding with a new kind of wheat. Red Fife was the name by which it was known in Wisconsin and Minnesota.

Wheats grown previously at Red River were a soft kind, like White Russian and Club. Settlers were unfamiliar with any other kind. They might have wished for more of the same, but they had no choice so they took the Red Fife and hoped for the best.

Of special interest, unrecognized by the Manitoba growers of the time, was the fact that this new wheat, imported from the United States, was really a variety of Canadian origin, bearing the name of a Scot who settled on the Fourth Concession of Otonabee Township, a few miles east of Peterborough. The Perthshire Fifes arrived about 1820, cleared the hardwood bush, struggled with stubborn stumps and made a home. In time, the son, David Fife, married and took over the farm. With an admirable desire to improve farming performance, he conducted a search for a better kind of spring wheat. Locally grown strains left much to be desired, since they were poor as yielders and highly susceptible to various plant diseases.

With a Scotsman's conviction that all good things come from Scotland, David Fife obtained some Scottish samples of wheat for testing. The result was completely unrewarding; grain from the experimental plantings was no better than wheat grown on the Fife farm in previous years. But as a Scot is never easy to discourage, Fife sent again, writing, this time, to a friend working as a clerk in Glasgow.

"I'd be glad to try anything new," he wrote, "If you can manage it, you might get me a sample of wheat from some cargo coming from Northern Europe."

The obliging friend went strolling along the Glasgow waterfront when wheat from Danzig was being unloaded. It looked like good wheat, but how was he as an onlooker to obtain the handful wanted for Fife in Canada? Pilfering was a crime for which a man could pay dearly. It seemed impossible to escape searching eyes. But Scots are ever resourceful people. Finding an excuse for walking on the ship's deck, the Glasgow man allowed his hat to be blown from his head, to fall into the hold containing wheat.

Nobody could justly deny a man his right to attempt recovery of lost personal property and Fife's friend climbed boldly into the compartment where his hat was resting on the wheat. His actions did not escape public attention, but he was playing his part skillfully and in the struggle to capture the hat he caught some kernels in the lining.

He put on his hat and went on his way. At home that night he carefully shook the wheat from the inner folds of the lining, placed the kernels in an envelope and mailed it to David Fife at Peterborough, Canada—"With best wishes."

The new seed arrived in time for spring planting in 1841. Fife placed it in a well-tilled part of his garden where there would be the benefit of a good fence to keep wayward cattle at a proper distance. Sharing her husband's interest in finding a better variety of wheat for their Ontario conditions, Jane Fife accepted responsibility for the little plot and weeded it and watered it faithfully.

The immigrant wheat germinated and started well enough, but seemed to grow indifferently. As heads appeared, they were small, and Fife was discouraged. Then his attention was drawn to a single wheat plant which seemed quite different. This one—product of a single seed— had stooled to send up five healthy stalks and each stalk had a big head, filling impressively. Hopefully, David and Jane Fife studied the heads from this plant, thinking the seed might be what they wanted.

The beautiful golden heads were almost ready for harvesting when one of Fife's perpetually hungry oxen broke the garden gate and advanced directly upon the row of experimental wheat. Mrs. Fife was busily preparing the noonday meal for her husband when she saw the ox rapidly devouring the best heads. The lady dashed frantically from her kitchen, shouting and waving her apron to frighten the offending animal away. After the ox retreated to the barnyard, Mrs. Fife, ready to weep, halted to survey the damage. It appeared at first that the ox had consumed all five of the good heads from the superior plant, but closer examination showed one head surviving. Four heads of the good and promising wheat had been eaten; just one remained.

Even that single head of handsome wheat might be worth keeping, Fife and his wife reasoned. They proceeded to build a barrier around it to ensure against any ox getting at it again. The head filled well, and the plump and heavy seeds caused it to bend gracefully. When its color indicated maturity, David and Jane Fife cut it from its stem, dried it in the sun and then rubbed out the hard, red kernels, making sure that not one was lost. The sample appeared attractive. Fife folded it in an envelope to await the next planting.

The next year, 1842, the short row of test wheat—all from one parent seed—looked better than anything Fife had seen. Double precautions were taken against invading oxen and the harvest yielded a pint of plump, red seed. Every succeeding year provided a bigger volume of seed, and neighbors who watched Fife's successes wanted some of the new strain for planting. The Otonabee Agricultural Society recognized the wheat's superiority and bought 260 bushels for local distribution. They paid the huge price of $2 per bushel for it.

The good wheat was red and so was Fife. It was logical enough to call it Red Fife. With that name it spread across Ontario, winning popularity on its merits: attractive appearance, high weight per bushel, high yield, and good quality for gristing and bread making.

Naturally, an international boundary cannot halt the spread of a superior grain variety any more than it can stop the transmission of a good idea. Red Fife was accepted in Michigan, then in Illinois and Wisconsin and farther west. American growers cared nothing about the story of the Scottish settler's search for better wheat, but they recognized variety merit when they saw it. When grasshoppers destroyed all the wheat growing at Red River and purged the nondescript kinds cultivated previously, settlers seeking fresh seed supplies from south of the border for the Selkirk colony returned with Red Fife.

To settlers on the long and narrow farms fronting on the Red and the Assiniboine Rivers, the name of Red Fife meant nothing. That it had originated north of the international boundary was unrecognized, just as the fact that it had come from a single seed which had been caught in a Glasgow man's hat received no attention. Those early farmers had no time for sentiment, but they would watch the performance of this new wheat and judge it accordingly.

It was not long before the Selkirk people realized that circumstances had brought them fortune; Red Fife wheat loved the western soil. It was not an early maturing variety and there was still the risk of serious loss from early frosts, but otherwise, this wheat, with a romantic beginning, far surpassed anything grown previously in the Manitoba area and even surpassed the best that it had been able to do in Ontario where development took place.

It was for this wheat, Red Fife, to demonstrate the true greatness of western soils, and then to contribute in a substantial and complex way to still more suitable varieties.

PART II

FRONTIER FERMENT

CHAPTER IX

❧

THE DAWN OF A NEW DAY

❧

October 21, 1876! A primitive sternwheeler splashed away from a shaky landing on the Fort Garry side of the Red River, carrying the most momentous cargo in western Canadian history—perhaps in Canadian or North American history. The boat, resembling a floating warehouse more than a sleek ship, was Jim Hill's *Selkirk*. The cargo consisted of 857 bushels and 10 pounds of Red Fife wheat, the first to be shipped from the new West. For anybody with sentiment for Canadian history and Canadian industry, that October date would seem to justify annual recognition in one form or another.

In many respects, it was a year of unusual significance. It was the year in which the first cattle were released to rustle a range-living and test a western winter at Fort Macleod.[22] This experiment marked the birth of prairie ranching. It was the year of the bloody Custer Massacre beside the Little Big Horn River, Montana, when Sitting Bull and his Sioux braves annihilated an imposing United States' force under General George Custer. As the year of the first wheat shipment from the West, it had the character of a fresh start for the growers, a year of beginning again.

The supply of Red Fife wheat, brought in at great cost and even greater inconvenience, had been apportioned in small lots to as many farmers as wanted it. Nobody was interested in planting more than a few acres because the only market which growers had known was the one created by strictly local appetites. The demand for gristing grain was limited, and there seemed no purpose in growing more wheat than settlers and a few fur traders could eat. Most farmers had no thought of planting more than three or four acres. Any person with six or eight acres of wheat was seen as a big operator.

As if to give the new variety a chance to show what it could do, the grasshopper menace disappeared. Growing conditions were favorable. Even with the small Manitoba acreage it became apparent that farmers would have wheat to exceed what the local mills could take. Concurrently, the Ontario crop was poor, and farmers there concluded that their wheat was deteriorating and a change of seed was needed in order to recover vigor and higher yields. It was a principle similar to that of changing herd bulls every few years. Their preference was for seed from an area with northern climate, capable of transmitting early ripening qualities and vitality. Farmers in Illinois were asking for seed from Minnesota. Simultaneously, men directing the Toronto seed business of Steele Brothers resolved to secure a supply of Manitoba wheat for distribution in the eastern trade. It was a bold decision, bordering on recklessness, because of the time element and the unknown factors of quantity and quality involved.

Not until after the poor Ontario crop was harvested were the eastern seedsmen able to confirm their plan. By that time, lateness of the season coupled with total lack of railroads or other direct communications raised huge barriers. Any hope for success depended upon R. C. Steele, junior member of the firm and later president of Steele Briggs Seed Company, being able to get to Winnipeg quickly and make the wheat purchases with the least possible delay. He could travel by way of Chicago and St. Paul to the end of United States' rail at Fisher's Landing in Minnesota, and from the latter point he could go to Winnipeg by riverboat. He obtained a ticket for passage, hoping to arrive early in October.

The river cruise, however, would take at least three days. Fearing river freeze-up before the needed wheat had been purchased and shipped out, Steele sought some way of reducing his traveling time and learned that he could save a few hours by abandoning the boat trip and taking to team and wagon. This he resolved to do. His first stop, after Fisher's Landing, was at Grand Forks in North Dakota, thirteen miles away, but the pause was a brief one—just long enough for feeding the horses—because Steele saw his trip as a clear race against time. Leaving Grand Forks at six o'clock in the evening, he drove the remaining 150 miles to Winnipeg, arriving at exactly twelve o'clock on the second night, precisely thirty hours later. They were thirty hours of continuous driving, save for the time taken to change horses.

In Winnipeg, where people were finding it difficult to accept the new name for Fort Garry, the young seed merchant made the acquaintance of David Young of the local firm of Higgins and Young, "Dealers in Boots and Shoes, Crockery and Glassware"—and just about any merchandise promising profit.

Yes, David Young would accept the assignment to buy 5,000 bushels of wheat or as near to that amount as available supplies would allow.

From October 13 until October 21, the *Manitoba Daily Free Press* carried the Higgins and Young announcement: "Cash for choice wheat to export to Ontario . . . 80 cents per bushel."

For Higgins and Young there was a commission of five cents a bushel; hence the cost to Steele Brothers, as shown on the bill of lading, was eighty-five cents per bushel for the wheat, plus thirty-five cents a bushel for freight, and twenty-six cents each for cotton bags.

Manitoba farmers, hearing of the unprecedented cash offer, responded eagerly, assessed their wheat stocks, and determined how much they could spare. Wives, with no less enthusiasm, held the bags while husbands shoveled. As loaded carts converged upon McMillan's Mill on Post Office Street, close to the river, farmers wondered if the Toronto money, with which they would be paid, was genuine. Dealing in dollars was a new experience. Although the settlers saw little cash in any form, most transactions had been conducted in English pounds and shillings.

But nobody had much to sell and it became quite clear that the country stretching from Red River to the Rocky Mountains could not fill an order for 5,000 bushels of wheat, regardless of the amount of Toronto cash offered. The country of 1876 did not have that much wheat—just 857 bushels and 10 pounds.

The biggest single contribution to the historic order was made by G. R. Miller of Kildonan who delivered 204 bushels. He received settlement amounting to $163.20. His neighbors wondered what he would do with it all. Next in volume of sales were H. Soar of St. John, who was paid $123.20 for 154 bushels, and R. Black of Springfield, who received $81.60 for 102 bushels.

Others delivering wheat included: J. W. Carleton, Clear Spring (80 bushels and 10 pounds); D. McDonald, Springfield (94 bushels); John Spear, Springfield (44 bushels); John Riech, St. Paul (40 bushels); F. Dick, Springfield (35 bushels); Alex Gibson, Springfield (33 bushels); T. B. Robinson, Rockwood (32 bushels); Neil McLeod, Victoria (22 bushels); and John McIvor, Greenwood (17 bushels and 45 pounds).

According to the *Manitoba Daily Free Press* of October 23, 1876, "Mr. Steele who is a seedsman of long experience, is highly satisfied with the samples furnished." Glad to have a news story of such unusual character, the editor made the most of it. He noted that "wheat from a northern district where the season is short carries its habit of quick ripening with it when sown in a southern district where the season is longer." This would lead to bigger demand and bigger orders for "seed," the editor assured.

"In the near future enterprising seedsmen will have to send their buyers here in time to make their purchases more leisurely and in time for large shipments before the close of navigation."

While praising Mr. Steele, as purchaser, and David Young, who acted on behalf of Higgins and Young in assembling the shipment, the editor displayed some of the vision to which all writers aspire. This, he told local people, might very well be a transaction of historic importance, something "worthy of remembrance when in the not far distant future, our shipments amount to millions of bushels."

The precious wheat was tied in 412 new cotton sacks and piled carefully on the riverboat. Then, with a feeble toot from the ship's steam whistle, the *Selkirk* drew away, upstream. What the few bystanders witnessed on that slightly frosty October morning, whether it occurred to them as a possibility or not, was the first trickle of what was quickly to become a torrent of wheat leaving the West for distant markets.

By traveling long hours and making the best use of time, Steele just managed to get his wheat out before the river froze over; forty-eight hours after the cargo arrived at Fisher's Landing, Red River navigation ended for the year. But the Manitoba wheat was then well on its way, going by rail to Duluth, lakeboat to Sarnia, and finally, rail to Toronto.

Ontario people studied the quality of this Manitoba product and uttered words of surprise and admiration. Eastern millers were anxious to secure a sample for testing in their plants. The milling result brought astonishment. Could Manitoba furnish more wheat of this kind? men wondered. At once the proposals for construction of a transcontinental railway to link the East and the West assumed more merit.

Winnipeg's only tangible reminder of the initial shipment of wheat is a bronze plaque hanging in the hallway of the Legislative Building. When the Canadian Seed Growers' Association held its convention in Winnipeg in June, 1932, the loading of the first wheat on a riverboat was re-enacted and a suitable bronze plate fixed to a large granite boulder at the riverbank site of McMillan's Mill was unveiled with appropriate ceremony. But on two occasions, men with more sentiment for scrap metal than for the momentous events of Canadian history forced the plaque from its base and took it away.

Wisely, the third plaque was placed where there would be less temptation to riverbank denizens. The great stone upon which the original metal was secured became buried beneath one of the dikes constructed to keep "Old Man River" in its place.

The editor, in his wisdom, believed Manitoba's principal role would be in furnishing wheat for seed purposes rather than for milling. In this opinion he was wrong, but he was not wrong when he saw the initial shipment as one possessing great significance, both locally and nationally. The wheat trade was to grow at a spectacular rate and all of Canada was to benefit. Indeed, the twenty-first day of October in every year should not pass without a pause to recognize the birth of a great industry and its remarkable growth after 1876.

That historic shipment of Red Fife wheat provided the best advertisement the new country could have obtained, and immediately, there was an invigorated interest in those homestead quarter sections, said to be available at ten dollars each.

CHAPTER X

༺☙❦❧༻

BETTER PLOWS

༺☙❦❧༻

After being grown indifferently for more than sixty years, wheat was given a sudden importance in the Red River community through the prospect of sale for cash. The Toronto seed merchant said he would be back to buy more grain. The result was an acreage increase coupled with the exercise of more planting care than ever before in those parts. If buyers were serious about paying good money for wheat, every farmer along the two rivers wanted to be in on the transactions.

Anticipation of the new demand was at once an inducement to improve cultural practices and equipment. Tilling, planting, and harvesting techniques had changed only slightly during the life of the colony, still the only agricultural community of any consequence in the prairie area. John Deere had invented a polished steel self-scouring moldboard plow. However, walking plows with rough cast iron moldboards or wood moldboards tipped with iron were still used. They were little different from the first plow made in the settlement in 1824. John Deere was a young Vermont blacksmith who moved to Illinois. In 1837, when he looked at a broken sawblade from a near-by mill, he caught the inspiration of a polished steel plow. From that blade he fashioned a plow which was to change cultivation practices in a big part of the world, and be a particularly fine aid to men about to tackle the virgin western sod.

Either wood or iron, used in heavy soils, accumulated great wads of clay which made plows heavy to pull and rendered them incapable of doing work much better than work done by the ancient method of using digging sticks.

Some of the money obtained from wheat sold in the autumn of 1876 went to pay for plows of the new kind, available at St. Paul. With astonishing foresight, James Pickard, representing Verity Implements, had visited Fort Garry in 1870 and advised his company to devise a plow for the special needs of the heavy Red River Valley soils. The company brought out a walking plow known as Verity No. 14, one destined to become a prairie favorite.

Before long, every settler aspired to be an expert plowman. A crooked furrow became a matter of shame. Nobody wanted to be held responsible for fields lacking uniformity and finish. Plowing matches became popular. British Columbia had the first in the West—one at Saanich on Vancouver Island in 1869 and one at Chilliwack in 1872; Manitoba had one late in 1877. It must have been a most unusual season for Manitoba because the match was held on Christmas Day. As reported by the *Daily Free Press* of Winnipeg on January 9, 1878, the competitions were on the farm of David Adams and seven contestants were present. First prize, a steel plow, was won by William Micklejohn. Second prize, an iron beam plow, went to David Timlick. The event was the forerunner of wheat country contests which ranked in popularity with baseball and curling.

Still bigger changes were to come in plows. The *Saskatchewan Herald* of October 15, 1890, noted that "R. Wyld has in use a newly imported gang plough with which he turns over an average of six acres a day." It was but one of many changes leading, in a big part of the West, to practical displacement of plows by other types of cultivating implements. However, the great impact of the self-scouring plows must not be overlooked. To follow those two-horse walking plows cutting eight-inch or ten-inch furrows, pegtooth harrows were made in the settlement. In leveling and pulverizing the plowed land, they were reasonably effective. For people who had not heard of disc harrows, duckfoot cultivators, and rodweeders, they were quite acceptable.

Those pioneer farmers operating beside the Manitoba rivers had advanced beyond the use of spades and hoes for cultivation, but otherwise, most operations connected with production and harvesting were still performed laboriously by hand. Men carrying seed in pans or sheets suspended from their shoulders did the planting by scattering expertly as they walked back and forth in measured strides. It was the method used by men of early civilizations. To cover the scattered seed as quickly as possible in order to spare it from marauding pigeons and give it the best chance of germinating, farmers resorted to harrowing or merely turning cattle or sheep into the fields, hoping that tramping feet would press the seeds into firm and moist soil.

An adaptation was the mechanical broadcast seeder, generally mounted on a horse-drawn wagon. Such a seeder, described as a Gatling Gun Broadcaster, was used on the big Bell Farm at Indian Head in 1885, scattering seed on eighty acres per day, but the mechanical broadcast seeder did not gain general favor and soon disappeared.

A mechanical seed drill which would deposit the grain below the surface of the soil was invented by England's Jethro Tull about 1730. The idea came to him when he viewed the pipes of the organ in his church. But such horse-drawn drills did not appear in the new West for nearly a century and a half.

Harvesting implements followed a long evolutionary course. They began with simple scythes and terminated with self-propelled combines right where western agriculture had its birth. Cutting a crop by means of scythe or cradle—the latter being a scythe-like tool with upright fingers to catch and hold the grain plants—was a tedious operation, and it is not surprising that mowers and reapers were introduced earlier than seed drills. With one man cutting and depositing the cut material in loose bundles or gavels and another man binding, it was possible to work over three or four acres per day.

One of Scotland's churchmen, Rev. Patrick Bell, invented a horse-pushed reaping machine with cutter bar and conveyor canvass to deliver the cut crop at one side of the machine. About 1831, a young Virginian, Cyrus McCormick, made a better reaper, one which became the progenitor of binders coming later.

The first reapers in the West required the power of two horses to pull them and the attention of two men to operate them. One man drove and the other raked the cut grain off the table to deposit it on the ground for tying. A few machines of the kind were imported from St. Paul, Minnesota, before the Riel insurrection[23] but most growers continued for a few years to recover their small crops by the old hand methods.

The next type of reaper seen in Manitoba, a Marsh harvester, was introduced almost immediately after the first wheat was shipped out in 1876. It had conveyor canvasses to take the cut crop to an elevated table on which two men sat to tie the sheaves.

It was the achievement of automatic binding by means of a mechanical knotter that did most in preparing the way for extensive wheat production in the West. The first automatic binders used wire because it could be fastened with a twist while twine or cord needed a knot. Wire, though, presented difficulties in threshing and in the use of straw for feed. In 1877, an American farm worker, John Appleby, came up with a mechanical knotter which was later adopted by William Deering for incorporation in the binders of that name.

The *Daily Free Press* of August 19, 1878, was able to report binders being in use in Manitoba, no doubt the first in the West. "We understand," wrote the reporter, "That there are now in use in this province about 20 self-binding harvesters. They are naturally objects of considerable curiosity wherever introduced. The other day, the agent for the McCormick machine, Mr. T. A. Haslam, drove a representative of the Free Press to Mr. R. Tait's in St. James to see one in operation . . . As is generally understood, the binding is done with fine soft wire. The sheaves were all nice and shapely and strong enough for all purposes."

A year later, a binder was still a novelty, and the *Winnipeg Weekly Times* of August 22, 1879, reported: "On Monday afternoon quite a large number of citizens proceeded to Polson's farm near St. John's college to witness a Marsh harvester and self-binder. The trial commenced at half past three o'clock. G. E. Tiffany had charge of the machine which was drawn by two horses. Three rounds were made, the sheaves being bound in various sizes to show the capabilities of the harvester. Mr. Polson and two others also drove the machine and pronounced it a success . . . The wire used was gauge 20, twenty pounds on a reel. It is stated that between twelve and fifteen acres of grain can be cut and bound in a day by this machine."

A binder, with knotter designed for twine, appeared in Manitoba in 1881. A year later, William Cust took one to his farm at St. Albert, north of Edmonton. The binder had arrived and farmers put away their scythes and cradles, but the idea of a combine harvester had not escaped all notice as an item in the *Winnipeg Morning Call,* August 4, 1887, indicated: "Mr. Stevenson, manager of the Lowe Farm at Morris, and inventor of the steam plow, is now engaged in manufacturing an attachment to the implement which, if it is proved to be practicable, will create a revolution in farm work. . . . The idea conceived by Mr. Stevenson in this attachment is to cut the grain, thresh and bag it and plough the land at the same time. Mr. Stevenson has made a model of the attachment and is now having the machinery manufactured at the Vulcan Iron Works in this city. . . . When the whole machine is complete, it will only require two men and a boy to operate it."

A few stationary threshing machines found their way north from St. Paul before the first wheat was shipped out in 1876. Most of the 857 bushels and 10 pounds of wheat bought by the Toronto seed firm had been threshed by means of flail, just as growers threshed in Old Testament times, employing nature's breezes to remove dust and chaff.

The early threshing machine was driven by horses, through that primitive apparatus known as a horsepower. It was a hard task for horses, since they were required to walk in a small circle for hours at a time. Oxen had been tried but without success, because, as settlers explained, the cattle became dizzy.

Two threshing machines with horsepower went over the long trails westward in 1878, one to Prince Albert and the other to the order of the Lieutenant-Governor of the Territories at Battleford.

As threshing methods were changing, so were sources of power. The *Daily Free Press* of July 9, 1874, reported: "The first steam thresher in the province is now in the warehouse. It was imported by L. R. Bentley for Farquhar McLean, Portage la Prairie." Gradually thereafter, steam relieved the tired farm horses of the grueling task of driving threshing machines—although there were numerous other heavy jobs for the horses.

Many more exciting changes were to be made in threshing techniques, but the frontier farmers had seen enough to assure them that machines would be available to support them in any expanded wheat-growing operations they might undertake.

CHAPTER XI

꧁ ☙ ꧂

PREPARATIONS FOR BIGGER THINGS

꧁ ☙ ꧂

Eastern buyers came in numbers in the autumn of 1877, behaving very much like any other satisfied customers. Their return coincided exactly with the signing beside the Bow River, far to the west, of the last major Indian Treaty, Blackfoot Treaty Number Seven.[24] It coincided, also, with the first clear and tangible evidence that the West was to get a railroad.

This time farmers near Winnipeg had more wheat, and the purchasers had more money with which to buy wheat. About 20,000 bushels were bought and bagged and loaded on riverboats to be taken upstream on the Red, then overland to the Great Lakes, and finally, to eastern Canada by lakeboat. Moreover, some of the wheat bought at Red River that autumn and loaded out on October 17 was for Barclay and Brand of Glasgow, Scotland, the first grain of any kind to be shipped overseas from the fresh western soil.

As the outlook for sales of western wheat brightened, men sitting in public places at Ottawa were reminded that in anticipation of an expanded trade, the country's preparations were far in arrears. For too long, government policy carried the imprint of pessimists who were still quoting George Simpson's words about the West's unsuitability for anything except furs and John Palliser's that the prairie country was an extension of "the Great American Desert." They also quoted Bishop Taché,[25] who wrote in 1868: "For my part, as there are extremely great difficulties in the way of colonizing the few points in this vast territory capable of cultivation, I acknowledge frankly that I would as soon—perhaps preferably—see the country remain as it is—as see it change."

In spite of these derogatory words returning to haunt the reputations of some otherwise great frontiersmen, the mists of superstition and misinformation were slowly being lifted. Public officials were accepting the necessity of a land survey, a settlement policy, and a railway to connect the East and the West.

Land surveyors with their steel chains and air of authority made their clumsy appearance near Red River in 1869. Their arrival thoroughly antagonized the Métis, squatting on long, narrow river lots which they considered to be their own by right of occupation. On July 10 of that year, John Stoughton Dennis was instructed by the Department of Public Works, Ottawa, to proceed to Red River and prepare recommendations for a land survey. A couple of months later, on September 23, the Federal Government approved by order in council the Dennis recommendations based on townships nine miles square, each with sixty-four sections of 800 acres and additional allowance for roads. With a minimum of delay, work started at the 49th parallel, near Pembina, with the principal meridian extending northward from a point about ten miles west of Pembina. But when the surveyors moved onto land beside the Red River, angry Métis ordered them to leave and never return. There was a showdown on André Nault's farm on the east side, a sort of preliminary to the Red River insurrection[26] in which Louis Riel played the leading part.

After the trouble ended, the survey plan was changed to embrace the now-familiar thirty-six-section township. Dennis was appointed to the post of Surveyor-General, and work was pursued with the vigor of men in a hurry. The critics seemed to transfer their attention to the proposed transcontinental railway.

It should have been clear enough: If wheat was to be grown and exported in any substantial quantities, a railway was needed to move it. But those who found delight in blocking a railroad scheme were loud in their arguments, most of them asking if this land, so recently a buffalo pasture, was really worth the cost of construction. There were editorials, like one in Henry Labouchere's *London Truth* of September 1, 1881, declaring this to be "a country frostbound for seven or eight months in the year." As for the Dominion as a whole, the editor saw it as "a fraud all through and destined to burst like any other fraud."

In spite of skeptics, plans for railway construction were being drawn seriously, and for the next few decades, railroad history was interwoven with the story of wheat. The riverboat *Selkirk*, before taking on a cargo of wheat in that autumn of 1877, discharged, on the St. Boniface side of the Red River, a shipment of freight which captured local interest more than anything since Louis Riel's New Nation. It consisted of a railway locomotive, a few flatcars, and some lengths of railway steel.

Although the West was still without a railroad, it now had the component parts for a train and the promise of more to come. The locomotive was already christened Countess of Dufferin (Lord and Lady Dufferin had intercepted the *Selkirk* as they were homeward bound to Ottawa after a visit to Manitoba). The Countess of Dufferin—locomotive —was quickly put to work laying steel southward toward the international boundary.

That pioneer locomotive, which ultimately found a permanent place of honor in front of the Canadian Pacific Railway depot in Winnipeg, did fine service, first in construction and later in hauling settlers into the country and wheat out of the country.

On December 5, 1878, the *Daily Free Press* was able to report, jubilantly: "The last rail is laid—the last spike is driven. Manitoba, after many vexatious delays which we can now afford to dismiss without a thought, is now connected by rail with the outside world." Five days later, the same paper had another report on progress: "The first regular train on the Pembina branch arrived at St. Boniface shortly after eleven o'clock on Saturday night [December 7] with about twenty passengers."

There was ample incoming freight to keep the new rail facilities occupied but not so much outgoing freight. A quantity of wheat was bagged and ready for loading, some of it having come by riverboat from the expanding settlement at Portage la Prairie. Earlier in that year, the *Daily Free Press* (April 9, 1878) reported 30,000 bushels of wheat stored at the Portage, "awaiting shipment down the Assiniboine."

Within the next year, Canadian Pacific rails reached Winnipeg from the east and at once wheat began to move toward the Head of the Great Lakes and Montreal. Faith in the goodness of western soil mounted rapidly. There was still the risk of crop failure, owing to early fall frost or drought or grasshoppers, but the soil was fertile and in most years wheat could be expected to mature. Farmers were aiming to bring bigger acreages under cultivation.

While confidence in the potential of western soil was rising, so was the flour miller's esteem for the quality of western wheat. Changes in milling practice came at a most opportune time to the advantage of western spring wheats.

Red River people had opportunity to know all about grinding by means of millstones. At first the grinding was done by hand, then by the power from that famous windmill which crossed the Atlantic Ocean three times before being set up to serve the settlers. Originally sent from England about 1815 on Lord Selkirk's instructions, it was received by colonists with no mechanical experience and baffled all attempts to set it up for operation. It was returned to England where it remained in storage for ten years before being sent again to Rupert's Land. On the occasion of its second trip to the New World, the windmill was accompanied by an expert who deftly put it to work to capture power from the winds of Assiniboia and displace the old hand-operated querns.

But the important thing in the seventies was the adoption of Hungarian rollers instead of stones by millers in the East and overseas. As long as the manufacturers used stones, winter wheats gave a whiter flour and enjoyed greater popularity than spring wheats. Although winter wheat was the first kind tried in the Selkirk Settlement, it failed, and Red River farmers were satisfied to struggle with spring varieties and accept the extra amount of bran which could not be removed from the ground product. Actually, the new settlers had no objection to some dark color in their flour and bread; only those people in more sophisticated communities demanded white flour, and growers have always been wise enough to seek consumer favor.

The new steel rollers tended to crush the kernels rather than grind them, making it easier to effect separation of bran and germ from flour. Thus, it was possible to remove much of the millers' former objection to spring wheats. Having used western spring wheats in the new rollers, millers liked them and wanted more. British millers sought a blend of spring and winter wheats and supplies from the new West were favored.

There is evidence that the Ogilvie Flour Mills Company was the first to use the Hungarian rollers on this continent. Company records show Alexander Walker Ogilvie making a study of the Hungarian process in 1871, with the new steel rollers being installed to replace millstones at the Ogilvie Mill at Glenora, Ontario, soon after. When Ogilvie built a commercial flour mill at Winnipeg in 1881, it was equipped with the steel rollers.

At last, a combination of circumstances worked to project western wheat into a position of prominence. The result, as shown by production figures, was quite dramatic. Although the West had less than 1,000 bushels to sell in 1876, it had 20,000 bushels in 1877, about 46,000 bushels in 1878 and 101,000 bushels in 1879.

Every year produced something new, and bigger than the last. The first export wheat shipment to be carried to seaboard by an all-Canadian route was made in 1884 by Thomas Thompson. It consisted of 1,000 bushels of Number One Hard. It was sacked, sent by rail to Port Arthur, by lakeboat from there to Owen Sound, by rail to the eastern port and ocean vessel to Glasgow, Scotland, making the complete journey from

Brandon—already seizing the title of Wheat City—in twenty-one days. In being consigned to Glasgow, this Red Fife wheat was going to the Scottish city from which a parent seed captured in a Scot's rebel hat had been sent in an envelope to David Fife, Peterborough, just a few decades earlier.

The acceleration in wheat output could not go unnoticed in the East and in other countries. Those who undertook to interest prospective immigrants found tasks lightened as western wheat gained recognition. The term "Free Land" had a magnetic ring about it at any time, but when there was explanation that the Free Lands in western Canada would grow wheat of the highest order, the candidate's interest could be transformed to eagerness. Wheat meant flour; flour meant bread, the stuff needed to sustain human bodies. Everybody understood. The western stage was set for a homestead rush.

CHAPTER XII

THE RUSH FOR HOMESTEADS

Since Rupert's Land was purchased with borrowed money, the Government of Canada had to make the territory productive. Having undertaken to build a railroad to the west coast, the Canadian Pacific Syndicate was equally anxious for people and production. A generous land policy provided the inducement. When word of Free Land finally echoed around the world, the response, although not instantaneous, built up to gold rush proportions.

The first homestead regulations were authorized by order in council in 1871. Any head of a family or person twenty-one years of age or over, with the financial resources to pay a ten-dollar fee, could file on the homestead of his choice, and move to occupy it immediately. Moreover, there was almost the whole of what became Manitoba, Saskatchewan and Alberta from which to make selection.

Before qualifying for patent on the quarter section, a homesteader was required to fulfill certain specified conditions with respect to period of residence, cultivation, and other improvements. In other words, the homesteader had to show proof of good and serious intentions. The "homestead duties" did not present serious obstacles. Most of those who filed on land resisted temptations to abandon the struggle to gain ownership. For a price of $2.00 or $2.50 per acre, a homesteader might obtain a pre-emption on a second quarter section of Crown Land.

For the first few years after the homestead regulations were announced, entries were not heavy. The country was still untested and the absence of a railway discouraged most prospective settlers. There were those, nevertheless, for whom danger and inconvenience held no terror, people who would not wait for rails or even trails. The first to file was John Sanderson, who became well known on the Portage Plains. Coming from Scotland, he was at Fort Garry when the Dominion Land Office opened for business, and his application was for the N.E. of 35, 12, 7,[27] a quarter section he had not seen up to that time. Having parted with the necessary ten dollars from his savings, Sanderson's next problem was to locate the land—and that could be difficult. Leaving Fort Garry, he drove a wagon and pair of half-broken oxen. After much argument with oxen and much searching of survey stakes, he located the quarter section for which he had made application, and was reassured to find it had good soil.

West of the Manitoba boundary, the first homestead patent was granted in April, 1883, to Thomas McKay of Prince Albert, and the next to Thomas Cavanough who settled near Fort Qu'Appelle.

It was nice to have a quarter of a million square miles of country from which to make a homestead selection, but such scope for choice could not be expected to last. In 1879, the Government adopted a policy of land subsidies to encourage railroad construction, and at once withdrew, for this purpose, all the odd-numbered sections. From the 100,000,000 acres so reserved, the Canadian Pacific Syndicate was to get 25,000,000 acres within twenty-four miles of its main line, also a cash subsidy of $25,000,000. The land grants represented greater government generosity than anybody at that time could recognize. In 1896, this form of subsidy was withdrawn, and railway companies were called upon to make their selection of lands to which they could establish claim.

Thus, one way or another, the homesteader's range of choice was substantially cut down. The C.P.R. officials took some of their land in blocks to facilitate irrigation development, but even after 1908 when the odd- and even-numbered sections were again offered for filing, most townships contained Hudson's Bay Company land, C.P.R. land and school land which was not available for homesteading.

The Hudson's Bay Company, by its territorial surrender in 1869, was to receive, in addition to cash payment, one-twentieth of land south of the North Saskatchewan River. Because a 36-section township was not conveniently divisible by 20, the Company was granted all of sections 8 and 26 in every fifth row of townships and all of section 8 and three-quarters of 26 in other townships. In the rather typical township, as early settlers knew it, sections 11 and 29 were marked as school land; section 8 and three-quarters of 26 belonged to the Hudson's Bay Company; other odd-numbered sections might be claimed by the C.P.R. and the remaining land was open for homestead entry.

Nobody really expected the rush for homestead land to start like a field of sprinters. For the first couple of years after the Free Land policy was announced, homestead entries numbered fewer than 1,500. Communication was primitive, and it took a while for the information about opportunity in the Canadian West to reach people in other lands. Many people who did receive the message, no doubt, waited for reassurance of the kind which came, ultimately, from Professor John Macoun[28] who described himself as a "government explorer in the North-West." Macoun's optimism, in *Manitoba and The Great North-West*, was the best possible counter-influence to the doubts raised by George Simpson, John Palliser and Bishop Taché. When wheat in Ontario averaged fifteen bushels per acre, Macoun wrote, Manitoba would have twenty-three bushels, Edmonton over thirty bushels and Peace River forty bushels per acre.

Brimming with confidence in wheat, Macoun wrote: "Much might be written about the future and calculations made regarding the wheat production of years to come, but such speculations are needless. In a very few years the crop will be limited by means of export, and just as the carrying capacity of the roads increases, so will the crop. No man can doubt this for a glance at the map will tell him that there is actually no limit but the want for a market to the wheat crop of the North-West."

Macoun anticipated the rush for homesteads, saying: "What in the spring of 1880 was a vast prairie covered with waving grass, will in the spring of 1882, be alive with settlers and its solitude and loneliness gone forever."

A salesman's optimism became the spirit of the West, and editors joined in proclaiming the greatness of the new wheat country. It was noted, for example, in the *Winnipeg Sun* of October 7, 1881, that: "Wheat at Emerson has reached 93 cents per bushel, thus giving the farmer a direct return of about $35 per acre, and this in a country that has only to be tickled with the plough to laugh into the harvest. The settlers may congratulate themselves on comparing their lot with that of the toilers among the stumps and stones in Ontario, where half of that income is above the average."

Groups of hopeful people from far lands were becoming more numerous. Mennonites, knowing something of prairie agriculture in Russia, were the first newcomers to choose the plains for their operations. Fifteen hundred came in 1874 and 3,500 in the next year, most of them settling on seventeen townships between the Red River and Pembina Mountain. They were serious people, eager to grow wheat. From this community, settlers went in later years to found colonies in Saskatchewan and Alberta.

In 1875 a party of 285 immigrants from Iceland arrived at Winnipeg and then went to the Gimli district on the west side of Lake Winnipeg where the people could combine farming and fishing to their fancy. They were good citizens from their arrival. Manitoba soon had the largest community of Icelandic people outside the native island.

The Mormons from Utah came in 1887 to settle at Lee's Creek and found the town of Cardston. A large group of Germans came in 1889. With the completion of the Calgary-Edmonton railroad adjacent lands became instantly popular. In the single year, 1892, about 3,000 settlers took land there, over 600 of them from the United States. Britishers, Scandinavians, Hungarians, French, and others came. But it was not until Hon. Clifford Sifton became Minister of Interior in Sir Wilfrid Laurier's government in 1896 that the incoming volume rose to flood tide.

Bringing salesmanship on a grand scale to his determination, Clifford Sifton saw hopeful people by the thousands coming from east, west and south. Great masses came from the Balkans, from the Ukraine and other Central European countries, men in sheepskin coats, women with shawls and broad beams, young people with lonely faces. For the English-speaking immigrants like the Barr Colonists,[29] the country was no less strange and overwhelming.

The year 1913 was the biggest for immigration; 402,000 people came to make homes in Canada, more than one-third of them in the new West. In the fifteen years after Sifton launched his program, about two million people came to Canada, and a big percentage of them were landseekers who did not stop until they reached homestead country. Most of them came without knowledge of the English language, but they brought willingness to work and to live frugally. On the homesteads, they made log houses or sod houses and plastered them with clay and chopped hay. They constructed thatched roofs and accepted dirt floors. They were the homesteaders, a polyglot of humanity with common purpose, and they set about to make the virgin soil grow wheat and other crops.

By the end of the century, the total number of homestead entries on land which had been buffalo range until so recently, stood at 81,447 with the figures rising at an accelerated rate. Admittedly, a considerable number of those who filed, failed to meet the requirements and saw their homesteads canceled. Extremely dry years in the eighties brought discouragement, inducing a rash of homestead abandonments on the central plains. But most of those who came with serious purpose remained to obtain titles and spend the rest of their lives on the land.

Thirty thousand people filed on homesteads in 1905, and 41,869 in 1906. By 1910, the total for thirty-seven years was 389,932 homestead entries. The year of greatest activity was 1911 when 44,273 applications were filed. Then numbers declined rather rapidly, but by the end of 1913 over 500,000 individuals had entered for homestead land in the three Midwestern provinces.

Certainly, the rapid influx of homestead farmers accounted for a big part of the spectacular rise in wheat production. For the entire western area comprising Manitoba and the North-West Territories, land seeded to wheat in 1880 totaled only 57,000 acres, with a mere 6,000 of this in the Territories. Production was little more than a million bushels. But ten years later, the area harvested 16,459,000 bushels of wheat from 860,000 acres. Except when it was shrunken and shriveled by early frost, it was good wheat. The millers agreed. Western purpose was becoming clear.

꩜

CHAPTER XIII

BIG FARMS FOR WHEAT

꩜

If a quarter-section or half-section wheat farm could be a good thing, then a really big farm should offer a surer and faster route to fortune. That was the reasoning of a few pioneers like Major William R. Bell and Sir John Lister-Kaye who came to the country of homestead farms and set about to put their grand schemes into operation.

The idea was fine in theory, but all the big spreads, with the character of wheat factories, experienced serious difficulties and most of them ended in failure. With an extra measure of Scottish economy, Adam MacKenzie was not only the first of the bonanza growers but one of the more successful of the big operators.

Adam MacKenzie's father, Kenneth, with Presbyterian rectitude in his dealings and the stamp of the Highlands on his tongue, came to the Northwest in 1868. He plowed a furrow around 1,800 acres of his choosing, about ten miles west of Portage la Prairie. Adam followed three years later, driving horses and cattle from St. Paul in Minnesota, and after three years at Rat Creek he married and set out on a combined honeymoon and search for land. It has been told that he outdrove a government courier sent to Minnedosa to cancel a certain issue of Half-breed Scrip, and then succeeded in obtaining much of the land he wanted by trading shotguns for quarter sections. When he was in a position to plow a furrow around his land claims, Adam MacKenzie's holdings looked like a real estate empire.[30]

At first, MacKenzie's nearest neighbor to the west was Archie Mac-Donald at Fort Ellice,[31] 156 miles away. But preferring to be without close neighbors, MacKenzie continued to buy up near-by land as it became available. At tax sales he was always present and always bidding. At one such sale he bought a quarter section which, as he discovered to his surprise, was already in his ownership. He had simply forgotten that he had it.

In those years when it was the custom for municipal officers to relieve tax pressure by allowing land owners to perform one day of roadwork for each quarter section on the assessment roll, MacKenzie was said to have enough land to keep one man and team doing roadwork for the entire year.

Everything Adam MacKenzie undertook was carried out on a great scale. When he freighted to Edmonton, he sent a train of carts which occupied a full half-mile of trail. His stables were stocked with enough horse harness to hitch a cavalry unit, and work horses were counted in the hundreds. He would buy any new machinery if it promised to reduce labor or save money. When he read, in 1889, about a new band-cutter and self-feeder for threshing machines being demonstrated at Portage la Prairie, he was determined to have one to help take off a crop amounting to well over a hundred thousand bushels of wheat. At the Winnipeg Exhibition a short time later, he saw a threshing machine with a good deal of plate glass in its construction to permit the operator to observe the internal workings in order to check losses of grain. He bought it, too.

Adam MacKenzie's big operations, which terminated with disposal of most of his land about 1908, did not prove anything, and arguments about the most efficient size of wheat farm continued. The ordinary quarter-section farmers looked on with no less astonishment when the Bell Farm at Indian Head emerged to dwarf everything around it. But Major Bell was not like Adam MacKenzie, who had no patience with waste and no hankering for grandeur. MacKenzie would laugh at the wild antics of a pair of irritated oxen until he learned that the turpentine a mischief-maker had applied to torment them had been taken from his farm supplies. Then he would shout: "Waste, it's got to stop." Major Bell, on the other hand, once instructed that forty-five new "self-binders" working in one big field in 1884 be halted for several hours for their inspection by a party of visitors arriving at Indian Head by train. An early frost in that autumn and a farm deficit of $244,000 brought such errors as delay at harvest time into sharp focus.

But the Bell operation as the first experiment in large-scale farming, west of the Manitoba boundary, was important. The Major was of United Empire Loyalist stock, born at Brockville, Ontario, in 1845. After service in the army—mainly fighting Fenians—he went west to search for opportunity. Traveling by train as far as the C.P.R. could carry him in 1881, he walked on from Brandon, studying soil as he made his way westward.

What attracted him most was an expanse of land marked only by a post on which an Indian skull had been suspended. Inspired by the idea of growing wheat at this point, Bell returned to Winnipeg and organized the Qu'Appelle Valley Farming Company.[32] As soon as the C.P.R. route was confirmed, he selected a block of land consisting of one hundred sections, extending seven miles north and three miles south of the proposed townsite. Land in the block was acquired from the Hudson's Bay Company and the C.P.R. at a cost of a dollar an acre and the Dominion Government agreed to let him have the homestead land. Thus Bell was able to gain control of everything in the block of one hundred square miles, except for small parcels held by three squatters who were loathe to move.

Farm work started in 1882 and, with oxen brought from Winnipeg, 2,700 acres of prairie land were broken and made ready for seeding in the following spring. Angus MacKay, coming in 1882, saw the first plowed land west of the Manitoba boundary on the Bell property. As soon as the snow had disappeared in the spring, Bell's men were seeding, using twelve broadcast seeders. When the seed was in place, forty three-horse sulky plows were sent to break more land, bringing the total for crop in 1884 to 6,000 acres. Men employed with breaking plows said some furrows were so long, a teamster could make only one round per day, aiming to be at the far end of the furrow for lunch time and back at the starting point by nightfall.

After a fair crop return in 1883—twenty bushels of Number One Hard wheat per acre—Bell indulged in the risky pastime of predicting the size of the next crop. It would be 120,000 bushels of wheat. Strangely enough, his guess was close. Threshed by steam-driven machines, the crop of 1884 amounted to 130,000 bushels but the sample was frosted and damp and much of the grain had to be fed to pigs. To add to the problems of the year, twenty-two horses were stolen from the stables in one summer night.

Before the seed for 1885 was in the ground, fighting against Riel's forces on the South Saskatchewan River, north of Saskatoon, appeared as a national emergency, and Major Bell answered the call for teams and wagons for freighting to the scene of conflict. Getting ten dollars per day for each man and team may have appeared more attractive than farming. Bell sent fifty outfits, leaving the farm short of men and power for field operations. But the circumstances taught a lesson by showing the value of summerfallowing in dryland farming. The year 1886 was especially dry, and the only good crops in the country were on land which Bell and Angus MacKay left fallow when their teams went to Duck Lake.

Company directors, however, were becoming tired of losses and ordered retrenchment. Bell left and turned to other things—peat bogs in Ireland, lumber in the Bahamas, coal in Alberta—remaining active until his death in Winnipeg in 1895. But the big Bell Farm lingered as a favorite topic for debate in wheat country for years.

Just as Bell Farm greatness was declining, along came Sir John Lister-Kaye, a little Englishman with the dynamics of a firecracker. Canadians saw him at Balgonie, east of Regina, where he was associated with Lord Queensbury on a 7,000-acre farm. There, in the spring of 1887, he sent thirty plows to the fields to prepare for the next seeding. When that next crop turned out well, Sir John became bloated with enthusiasm. His 7,000-acre farm was too small.

Having formed the Canadian Agricultural, Coal and Colonization Company, he obtained ten blocks of land, each 10,000 acres, along the new railway, about half of it from the Government of Canada and half from the C.P.R. He would produce wheat and other products and gain fortune on a scale never before witnessed. He would show how it was to be done. Warnings about the destructiveness of prairie drought fell on deaf ears. Sir John would find a way to beat the drought.

Five hundred Clydesdale horses were ordered from Ontario to pull plows through the sod in anticipation of the next season's crop. But 1889 was dry. Not even the doggedness of Sir John would make it rain. There was no crop. Sir John was not ready to admit defeat. He had an idea. Without waiting to know where the water would come from, he ordered pine tanks in Winnipeg, forty-four of them, each eleven feet long, two feet high and the width of a wagon bolster. The fleet of horse-drawn tanks was pressed into service in the summer of 1890, but the water from these containers made practically no impression upon the big fields. More than 110 tons of water would have been needed to provide even one inch of water on a single acre, and to treat the big fields in this manner was totally impracticable.

Sir John may have been unfortunate in timing his big experiment with wheat because the eighties, like years in the decade of half a century later, were distressingly dry; 1883, 1885, 1886 and 1887 brought crop failure somewhere on the prairies and 1889 was a year of widespread disaster, like 1937, drought year of drought years.

Reluctantly, Sir John gave up the idea of growing wheat on the extensive scale and turned to cattle and sheep. After buying 5,000 Powder River Ranch cattle wearing the 76 brand, he ordered 10,000 sheep to be driven in from Montana. Everything had to be on a grand scale and mistakes were big ones too. After nine or ten years of it, Sir John retired and manager D. H. Andrews formed a new company and took over the holdings.

Even more abrupt was the end which overtook the big Sandison Farm operation at Brandon, presided over by an unsurpassed showman, J. W. Sandison, also known as King Sandison and Gatling Gun Sandison. Manitoba claimed the title of Wheat Province; Brandon was becoming known as the Wheat City, and it suited Sandison to be the Wheat King of the World. While he spent lavishly and seeded 3,000 or 4,000 acres of crop, Brandon people looked upon him as a hero and editors praised his achievements. "Did you see the Sandison wagon parade from the Massey-Harris warehouse?" asked the editor of the *Brandon Sun* (April 14, 1892), who then added: "Well, it was good, but nothing to what it will be when he takes out his 17 Massey-Harris binders . . ."

But when Sandison returned in the spring of 1893 after wintering in England and Scotland, his creditors were waiting for him and the hero Wheat King quickly became an object of derision. An editor, who had sung the Sandison praise on many occasions, wrote: "It was known to many of the observing ones, for years past, that Sandison's methods of farming could not be made to succeed."

With debts totaling over a hundred thousand dollars and creditors growing impatient, Sandison just vanished, leaving the big farm to run itself. Of course there had to be some sort of settlement, and a monster auction sale of farm livestock and equipment was advertised for June, 1893. The sale lasted for three days and broke many records. An editor, with commendable hindsight, wrote: "Big farming will never succeed in this country."

CHAPTER XIV

❧

"PRAIRIE SKYSCRAPERS"

❧

Happy to have railroads being built to serve them, western farmers accepted, for a time, the heavy toil of loading wheat from wagons to freight cars by hand. The common practice was to handle wheat in two-bushel bags and dump them, one at a time, in a car spotted at a siding. A special knot was employed, quite universally, in tying the bags. To master the art of making it was fundamental education for many farm boys. It was like memorizing the Shorter Catechism and learning to tell a horse's age from the cups in its teeth.

It took 650 bags of wheat to fill a 1,300-bushel freight car. Hoisting 120 pounds per sack to shoulder height, hour after hour, was no job for anybody with weak heart or soft muscles. Nothing more was needed to make many hired men and settlers pause to wonder why they had not remained to hoe turnips in Ontario.

The immediate requirement to provide better shipping facilities was to have trackside storage at the loading end. The Canadian Pacific Railway Company indicated a willingness to build some sort of terminal storages at the Lakehead but showed no inclination to be in the business of providing local warehouse space. The first trackside storage facilities came in the form of "flat warehouses," inventions of businessmen whose main purpose was to establish a good and profitable connection with the expanding wheat trade.

The sprawling structures were nothing more than big granaries, some with roofs, some with nothing to protect the grain from rain and snow and hungry birds. Their appearance, unadorned by paint, added nothing to the landscape. But they did serve a purpose. Dividing walls permitted a series of small bins, all at ground level, of course. The only labor-saving equipment anybody thought to install consisted of an overhead track on which bagged grain could be moved along the passageway, and a small railcar on the floor to aid in the transfer of loose grain from bins to loading platform beside the track.

The general arrangement was a good deal better than nothing at all, but it left much to be desired. It offered little for the man who wanted to hold his grain in storage to await a better market. Having loaded a car when any were available, the farmer felt compelled to sell on the spot, "track basis," or ship to a grain merchant or terminal; in either case, he more or less lost control over the product.

The flat warehouse, although incapable of doing much to reduce the heavy lifting in loading cars, flourished for a few years after its appearance in 1879. It served the expanding wheat trade until the invention and introduction of the "endless cup conveyor". Grain elevators then had over-head storage bins from which grain could flow, by gravity, to freight cars spotted alongside. The first western elevator—a round one capable of holding 30,000 bushels—was built at Niverville in 1879. Two years later, a square elevator was erected at Gretna by the Ogilvie Milling Company. Acceptance of this upright type of elevator with square base was almost instantaneous. Looming like prairie skyscrapers, the new structures promised to rank with railroads in bringing convenience and benefit to the wheat country. Instead of bagging and shoveling, growers could simply drive into the elevators, weigh loads, dump them for overhead binning and promptly drive away for more grain.

The principle of perpendicular construction made it possible to rely upon gravity and the free-flowing character of wheat to carry out at least some of the elevator operations. From the wagon, bulk grain could fall into the elevator pit from which it would be elevated to one of a score or more of bins by means of an engine-driven belt equipped with metal buckets. Finally, from its overhead place of storage, the grain could be directed through spouts to fall in freight cars spotted on the track beside the elevator. Thus the hardship of unloading from wagons to warehouses and reloading on cars was removed almost completely.

By 1882, Manitoba people could count six grain elevators. Thereafter, elevator numbers increased rapidly. Away to the west, in what was to become the province of Alberta, the Brackman-Kerr Milling Company built an elevator at Strathcona—now South Edmonton—in 1896. Railway officials liked the prospect of these towering edifices dotting the wheat country and offered inducements such as free trackside sites to any individuals or groups of individuals who would build and operate elevators. They were also given monopolistic loading privileges.

By 1890, according to information compiled by Major H. G. L. Strange of Searle Grain Company,[33] the West had 90 elevators and 103 flat warehouses—83 of the former and 93 of the latter being in Manitoba. The 193 units had a combined storage capacity of 4,286,000 bushels. In the next ten years, nearly all new storage structures were in the form of elevators rather than flat warehouses. By 1900, there were 454 elevators and 126 flat warehouses in operation in the West. No longer were the flat warehouses being built, but a few of them survived as dilapidated storehouses used by coal and feed mercants for another forty or fifty years.

If western farmers were to benefit from savings made possible by water transportation on the Great Lakes, wheat would have to move by freight train to Port Arthur or Fort William, and from there by lakeboats to Montreal where cargo would be transferred to ocean-going vessels bound for Liverpool and other trading centers in the Old World. Such a combination, ensuring substantially greater economy in shipping costs than could be realized in all-rail freight, would necessitate elevators of another type at transfer points. Terminal elevators would have to be situated to allow a well-co-ordinated system of unloading cars and loading ships.

As soon as freight was moving by rail to the Lakehead in 1883, the Canadian Pacific Railway Company constructed terminal warehouses to accommodate the crop of that season. A steam barge bearing the name *Erin* drew alongside to be the first lakeboat to take on a wheat cargo. No consideration had been given to labor-saving methods. The 10,000 bushels of bagged wheat to fill the boat's hold were moved by dollar-a-day laborers pushing wheelbarrows. But better terminal accommodation had been planned, and while the *Erin* pulled away with the first grain cargo to cross Lake Superior work was started on the original lakeside storage to classify properly as an elevator.

"King's Elevator" was what people called the new terminal. By the time the crop of 1884 was threshed and rolling toward Port Arthur, the elevator, with bin room for 350,000 bushels, was ready to serve as the needed "coupling-pin" between freight cars and lakeboats, between the West of Canada and the East. The lakeboat *Acadian* docked alongside and became the first to load from an elevator spout at that location. Next year, 1885, a 1,000,000-bushel terminal was inviting business a short distance away at Fort William.

By 1890, total terminal elevator space at the two points beside Lake Superior stood at 4,500,000 bushels and was still expanding rapidly. One new terminal elevator after another was built and the Lakehead's "connecting-link" importance in the wheat trade has never been challenged. In recent years, the Twin Cities—Port Arthur and Fort William—

could show terminal elevator accommodation for over 100,000,000 bushels. The biggest single terminal could take about 9,000,000 bushels.

In recent years when Canada had to carry big surplus stocks of wheat, growers had reason to be thankful for the huge storage space available at Lakehead, Pacific, Churchill, and other terminal points. Canada's total terminal capacity at August 1, 1962, had grown to 154,930,410 bushels. When the figure of 367,471,300 bushels—the aggregate grain accommodation at country elevators—was added, it gave a grand total of well over 500,000,000 bushels and explained how the country could have a carry-over of 400,000,000 or 500,000,000 bushels of wheat at the end of a crop year with relatively little direct hardship to the growers.

Increasing storage capacity was not the only change of consequence at terminals. In 1905, a system of rapid unloading of cars was introduced. It coincided roughly with the Federal Government's rapid system of grain inspection. What became known as the "Fort William-Port Arthur Methods" in handling and inspecting grain won praise from many parts of the world and brought overseas visitors to study it.

The growth and improvement of terminal elevator accommodation were spectacular. So was the increase in country elevators whose towering shapes became so commonplace that they seemed to belong in the landscape of the Prairies. Artists, looking for local scenes, loved them; tourists, searching for towns and villages, saw them as landmarks; agricultural people, trying to make rapid calculations about the productivity of surrounding soils, counted the elevator units at the center.

In the year 1882, a total of six elevators served the Midwest of Canada; exactly eighty years later, Manitoba had 682 country elevators capable of holding 47,511,300 bushels; Saskatchewan had 2,877 elevators, good for 192,851,800 bushels; and Alberta had 1,639 with capacity of 123,189,700 bushels. Thus, the country elevator space in three provinces was 363,552,000 bushels. It represented an average elevator capacity of approximately 60,000 bushels.

It was not surprising that a visitor from Europe saw Canada's wheat country as "the land of elevators."

❦

CHAPTER XV

ANGRY GROWERS

❦

Farmers who knew all about the dead weight of wheat in two-bushel bags were happy to see the new elevators piercing their skyline, but the new methods of storing and loading were not to become general practice without some irritations and annoyances. Not many growers would retain the old shovel and sack techniques in delivering grain to freight cars if they could have confidence in the new elevator service using endless belts and gravity to move the product. But when the railroad company granted exclusive car-loading rights to the elevator operators, thus eliminating loadings from platforms and warehouses, growers complained loudly.

The new railroad policy was fine as a means of inducing elevator construction, but it irked farmers who resented a rule which would deny them an alternative in loading and leave them entirely at the mercy of operators who were suspected of overmuch greediness in buying and grading. Without the restricting rule, growers, almost without exception, would have put their wheat through elevators and paid the handling charges. Human nature being what it is, the new order made them demand the right to load cars when they wished by the old and laborious method—and save a few dollars.

When the growers' ire was raised, they could think of some additional reasons for complaint. Storage charges were too high. Both grades and sale prices were too low. It happened too often that a farmer bringing a load of good wheat to the elevator—perhaps Number One Northern—was told that all bins for the top grades were full, but the bins marked for Number Four wheat would still take a few loads. If the farmer would sell his Number One wheat at Number Four price, the elevator man would purchase. The grower, needing money immediately, generally agreed to the transaction. Just which bin actually received the Number One wheat, nobody except the elevator agent ever knew. Moreover, farmers needing money to pay bills were obliged to sell at the time of heavy fall deliveries, while the elevator operators were able to speculate and benefit.

The sore point was that elevator interests, enjoying a monopolistic position, appeared to be making the rules and taking full advantage. Farmers became increasingly angry, but they gained nothing by merely arguing with elevator agents whose answers were generally the same: "Take it or leave it." The alternative to delivery at an elevator was to haul the grain back to the farm to be stored or fed to the pigs.

Farmers turned to governments for help. James M. Douglas, member of parliament for Assiniboia, introduced a bill in 1898 to regulate grain handling and assure farmers of the right to load their grain from wagons to cars if that were their choice. The bill did not pass but it served to direct public attention to the grain growers' complaints. Another result came later with the appointment on October 7, 1899, of a Royal Commission to study and report on the grain trade.

Named to this first investigating body were an Ontario Judge, Mr. Justice E. J. Senkler, as chairman, and three Manitoba farmers, W. F. Sirrell of Glendale, William Lothian of Pipestone, and Charles C. Castle of Teulon. Owing to the chairman's illness, Mr. Justice Richards of Winnipeg was named to finish the assignment. Charles N. Bell, well known at Winnipeg, was secretary.

No time was wasted. The Commission reported in March, 1900, and supported the growers in their demand for complete freedom to ship and sell and recommended a uniform system of issuing grain tickets as an aid to protect farmers on grades and weights.

The Federal Government acted promptly, and passed the Manitoba Grain Act before the end of the year. Weight and grade standards were defined; and farmers were to have the right to load grain through flat warehouses or directly from wagon box to freight car if they chose. To see that farmer rights were observed, a grain supervisor was to be appointed. Growers were encouraged. To fill the new supervisory position, one of the Manitoba members of the Commission, C. C. Castle, was named.

It was a good effort and seemed to placate the irate farmers. But as time passed, the result of the new Federal statute was less than they had been led to expect. Elevator people who reacted to the Manitoba Grain Act by rushing to organize the North West Elevator Association—later called the North West Grain Dealers' Association—seemed to slip back into the old ruts, and farmers complained about being overdocked, undergraded, underpaid, and ignored when they requested cars for direct loading.

The year of 1901 saw an acute shortage of cars. It was at this point in wheat country history that the farm movement had its birth. There had been attempts at organization on earlier occasions, giving rise to the Manitoba and North West Farmers' Union, formed in 1882, and then the Grange, known also as the Patrons of Industry. But none possessed the qualities of long survival. Not only was there a car shortage in 1901, but the distribution clause in the Act was being ignored and hardly any cars were made available to the producers for over-the-platform loading. The situation was deteriorating.

W. R. Motherwell, a young homesteader near the Qu'Appelle Valley, wrote angry letters to the press and suggested the need for a farmers' organization to lend strength to demands. Encouraging him was his friend and neighbor, Peter Dayman. They resolved upon a call for action.

As it happened, Premier R. P. Roblin of Manitoba and Premier F. W. G. Haultain of the North West Territories had accepted invitations to be at Indian Head for a public meeting on December 18, 1901, when a proposal to add Assiniboia to the province of Manitoba was to be debated. Motherwell and Dayman noted that many people from outside points would be in town; it would be a good time for a discussion about organization. Together, the two men wrote letters to all the farmers whose names they could find. The people to whom the messages were addressed reacted with ready interest.

When the day set for the meeting arrived Indian Head streets were crowded with homesteaders. Many had driven horse and ox teams over long trails. Before the farm meeting ended, the initial step in founding the Territorial Grain Growers' Association had been taken. Motherwell was the provisional president. A constitutionally called meeting followed in a few weeks—February 1, 1902—and there Motherwell was confirmed in the office of leader, and farmers confirmed their intention to be heard.

There was still no indication that the grain handlers were impressed. Grading, weighing and docking were administered about the same as ever, and the car situation grew no better. Agents were neglecting to keep order-books as required by the Manitoba Grain Act. Farmers missed their turns while elevator agents obtained cars with relative ease. At least that was what farmers, who may have been magnifying their misfortunes, said.

Motherwell went to Winnipeg to discuss the whole matter with officials and won cheerful promises that things would be better. But they were not better and President Motherwell and his friends decided to force a test. Nobody thought the farmers would go to court, but these men from the homesteads were mad and determined. For the purpose of a showdown, a formal charge was laid against the railroad agent at Sintaluta, and farmers declared their complaints in sworn affidavits.

Again the men of the soil came to town in great numbers, this time to be present for the court hearing at Sintaluta. Some, from a distance, brought blankets and slept in their wagons; some bedded down in livery stable hay. In any case, they were not going to miss this moment of decision when the magistrate would deliver an important ruling affecting them all. They were not disappointed. The judgment was against the railroad agent; the penalty was a fine of fifty dollars.

Shocked by the decision, the railroad company appealed it, but the higher court upheld the magistrate's ruling. The growers were encouraged. Early in 1903, the first Manitoba Grain Growers' Association was formed at a meeting in Virden, and two months later the city of Brandon was the setting for the first provincial convention.

Things were moving along rapidly. Grain growing farmers were eager to gain more control over marketing. In the autumn of 1904, the Territorial Association authorized E. A. Partridge of Sintaluta to visit Winnipeg and conduct a one-man investigation of the operations of the Winnipeg Grain Exchange which had grown up as a local but powerful body. There could be no doubt that something of its kind to regulate buying and selling was needed, and Winnipeg, situated between the grain fields and the Lakehead, seemed a proper place for it.

Very early, the Winnipeg Board of Trade recognized the need, setting up its own Grain Exchange in 1883, but the institution, intended to exercise some control over buying and selling, did not get the support required and it failed. A short time later, however, leading grain marketing personalities met to form the Winnipeg Grain and Produce Exchange, thereby laying the real foundation for a body which served a long and useful purpose, and may not have deserved all the evil criticism directed at it over the years.

As Mr. Partridge—a man less patient than Mr. Motherwell—reported, his reception in Winnipeg had the coolness of an Arctic breeze and the Grain Exchange was "a house with closed shutters." When the Manitoba Grain Growers met in convention in 1905, Partridge recommended the formation of a farmers' grain marketing body. It was a bold proposal from an imaginative and bold farmer. A committee named to study the proposal returned with support for it. Growers would conduct their own marketing business right to, and including Winnipeg. The idea was approved, and after shares were sold in sufficient numbers, the Grain Growers' Grain Company was ready for business in 1906.

The road ahead was rough and treacherous. The farm organization bought a seat on the Winnipeg Grain Exchange, but in so doing, was buying only fresh trouble. Old members of the Exchange were hostile. They used the excuse that the co-operative principle of paying patronage dividends was tantamount to rebating part of the commission, and therefore, in violation of Exchange bylaws. On November 8, 1906, not long after purchasing the Grain Exchange seat, the farm company's trading privileges were rudely suspended. If Grain Exchange officials supposed they could keep the growers out of Winnipeg in this way, they were sadly mistaken. The Grain Growers' Grain Company came back stronger than ever, and then added to prestige and influence by obtaining a chain of country elevators from the Manitoba Government.

In 1911, the Saskatchewan Co-operative Elevator Company was organized with Provincial Government assistance. In 1913, the Alberta Farmers' Co-operative Elevator Company was formed, also with backing from the Government. In 1917, there was amalgamation of the Grain Growers' Grain Company and the Alberta Farmers' Co-operative Elevator Company to create the still bigger United Grain Growers' Limited.

Motherwell's angry farmers had advanced a long way.

CHAPTER XVI

⁓⊙⁓

HAIL THE MARQUIS

⁓⊙⁓

Red Fife wheat and prairie soil seemed to suit each other like young lovers. In winning recognition for the West, the introduction and acceptance of this great milling variety would have to rank with the benefits obtained from the land policy and the railroads.

Various other varieties were tried and grown, more or less indiscriminately. In the Selkirk colony, wheat was wheat, and settlers were ready to plant any seed they could obtain. Variety names—generally indicating origins—included Black Sea, Norway, Prairie du Chien, Club, White Russian, Golden Drop and Odessa Red. Red Fife, introduced when grasshoppers devoured Manitoba crops in successive years during the seventies, proved superior to all others and quickly displaced them. It yielded better than anything grown previously and won acclaim at home and abroad as the best of all wheats for milling and baking.

Even at that, Red Fife was far from being perfect. Growers wished it had a growing period shorter by at least a week or ten days. Superior milling qualities were of no benefit if the wheat did not mature. Too often, development of an otherwise fine crop was abruptly arrested by fall frosts striking when plants were still green, leaving the grain kernels shrunken and light, and good for nothing better than pig feed.

With the spread of settlement and cultivation to more northerly areas, the dangers of crop damage because of early fall frosts increased. Clearly, there was need for a variety combining the suitability, yield, and milling qualities of David Fife's wheat, with a saving of at least a week in time needed for maturity. Unfortunately, such a variety did not exist. Fortunately, Dr. William Saunders, first Director of the Dominion Experimental Farms, had a plant breeder's vision of what might be done to create something completely new to fit the need.

Even before his appointment as director, William Saunders had been active and successful as a plant improver. He had developed a number of new and better varieties of raspberries, gooseberries, and currants. Hon. John Carling, Minister of Agriculture in Sir John A. Macdonald's government, recognized the value of experimentation and instructed Saunders to conduct a survey of the experimental farms and stations in the United States. He carried out the task and in his report to the Minister, tabled in the House of Commons on April 15, 1886, Saunders proposed a plan for a Canadian program. Before two months elapsed the House passed an Act giving authority for the establishment of five Experimental Farms. Dr. Saunders was appointed to direct the system and work went forward at the Ottawa site for a Central Experimental Farm. At the same time land was acquired for other Farms at Nappan, Brandon, Indian Head and Agassiz. To the position of Superintendent of the Indian Head Experimental Farm the Government appointed Angus MacKay, an 1882 homesteader with an intimate understanding of the needs among prairie grain growers.

The new director wasted no time in undertaking a search for better wheat varieties. He hoped to find something with strength where Red Fife was weak. From far-away India, Russia, Japan, and Australia came samples for growing and testing alongside Red Fife. Some were later in maturing than Red Fife and could be eliminated quickly; certain others were misfits on Canadian soil. But one of the Russian introductions, Ladoga, a bearded kind, appeared promising and western Canadian growers who tried it reported favorably. It was indeed earlier than Red Fife and yielded almost as well. However, to obtain milling and baking tests presented difficulties at that time. When the required carload of grain was finally submitted for testing in 1892, all hope expressed for Ladoga was at once dispelled. The flour lacked good bread-making prerequisites, and deeply disappointed, William Saunders turned his attentions elsewhere.

There was only one thing for it: attempt by the technique of crossing to combine the best characteristics of selected parent strains. Actually, hybridization of wheat varieties—effected by placing the pollen from the flower of one parent on the stigma of another whose stamens were removed—was started at the Central Experimental Farm in the summer of 1888. Using Red Fife as one parent and Ladoga or an Indian wheat like Hard Red Calcutta as the other, scores of crosses were made, with Dr. William and sons Charles E. and Arthur Percy conducting most of the delicate work. When milling tests eliminated Ladoga the crossbreeding efforts were intensified. During the summer of 1892 Dr. A. P. Saunders traveled across the

West, making wheat crosses at each of the three western Experimental Farms.

In due course, the harvested seeds from the various crosses were planted for tests at Ottawa and some strains appeared with sufficient merit to fill the Saunders men with encouragement. The most attractive of these were named Preston, Stanley, Huron, and Percy. The first two came from Red Fife and Ladoga parents, and the other two from White Fife and Ladoga. But, again, when proper milling and baking tests were made, variety defects showed up. It was apparent to the plant breeders that they had not yet found that Ideal Wheat of which they were dreaming.

Events took a new and important turn when, in 1903, Dr. Charles E. Saunders was appointed Dominion Cerealist. Because his father's other duties had become heavy, wheat breeding was receiving less attention than it warranted. The new Dominion Cerealist prepared to pursue the work with all possible vigor. Preparations were made to re-examine all the hybrid strains, some of which had been gathering dust on Ottawa shelves for a few years. The short test rows took on new interest in that spring season. With devotion and patience, Charles Saunders watched the wheat plants grow and mature and, with masterly understanding, he made single-head selections.

The head to impress him most was one from a Red Fife—Hard Red Calcutta cross made at Agassiz eleven years earlier, presumably by A. P. Saunders and Thomas Sharpe. The seed of this single head was planted carefully in 1904 and from it twelve wheat plants grew vigorously. Again, the strain showed good yield, and by the simple and primitive chewing test to ascertain gluten strength, it seemed as though it might have good baking qualities.

By the autumn of 1906, seed from this particular hybrid strain totaled forty pounds—forty precious pounds—and Saunders wanted to test it under the more harsh conditions of the West where it would have to grow to be successful. To whom should he entrust the responsibility for the test? He considered carefully and decided that the hard-to-convince Scot, Angus MacKay at Indian Head, would be the best referee.

Leaving Whitby, Ontario, in 1882, MacKay had journeyed westward by train to the end of steel at Oak Lake, walked on from there to select a section of land close to the only local landmark—an Indian skull suspended on a stake beside the trail. For his first crop, he had only eighteen acres cultivated and ready, but the Red Fife planted thereon gave him a return of forty bushels per acre. The next crop, in 1884, was severely frozen before it was mature; and MacKay threshed only pig feed instead of what might have been Number One Hard. In 1887, he helped to find a good location for the new Experimental Farm at Indian Head, then agreed to accept the post of Superintendent. Saunders at Ottawa and MacKay at Indian Head were to make the perfect working combination in the great search for better wheat.

Just before the planting season of 1907, Charles Saunders sent twenty-three pounds of the new wheat, about which he dared to be enthusiastic, and asked MacKay to plant it carefully and watch it studiously.

Even before the first planting, the priceless sample encountered near tragedy. From its resting place on a granary shelf, the bag of wheat was taken a night or two after it arrived—stolen, no doubt, by somebody interested in feed for his pigeons or hens. Naturally, MacKay was worried to the point of being sick. How could he explain such a loss to Charles Saunders? The Mounted Police might be called to conduct an investigation, but by the time the law officers completed their work, the wheat could be passing through the digestive tracts of somebody's poultry. Suspecting that the thief was a man working on the Experimental Farm, MacKay issued a written appeal, suggesting that the lost seed might very well hold the hope for an improved variety such as was needed by western growers. The granary door would be open that night, the writer of the appeal added, and nobody would be on guard. To MacKay's great joy, the bag of wheat was back on the granary shelf next morning, undamaged.

The new wheat grew well in 1907, and being at least a week earlier than Red Fife, it escaped a fall frost which damaged the other variety growing nearby. In each of the next two years, harvest results confirmed the wheat's superiority. Late in 1909, MacKay advised Saunders that he had complete confidence in the wheat and believed the time had come to share it with the western farmers. Carrying the name "Marquis" it was released in time for planting in 1910, but the supply was limited and the demand was great.

Earlier than Red Fife, Marquis could be grown farther north and was able to extend the wheat belt and give the West a promising potential as a producer. Having the very high milling and baking properties of Red Fife, it was wanted by millers both at home and elsewhere.

As quickly as seed became available, Marquis displaced the older varieties, including Red Fife. It began to look like the biggest single advantage to come to the Canadian economy. While it was spreading across the Canadian spring wheat country, it was doing the same in the northern districts of the United States. Growers south of the boundary saw Marquis as something better than they had and were eager to get it. About

200,000 bushels of Marquis were shipped to the United States in 1913. By 1917 more than 40 per cent of wheat planted in Montana, North Dakota, South Dakota, and Minnesota was Marquis. It established a debt which the United States plant breeders repaid some twenty years later by providing Thatcher for use in Canadian fields.

Marquis became the standard of quality for hard red spring wheat and held that enviable distinction for more than half a century. One way or another, its contribution to the economy of the nation was beyond calculation.

PART III

❧

RESOURCEFUL GROWERS

Herman Trelle (left) and J. C. Mitchell, western Canadian winners of world championships for wheat.

Angus MacKay, superintendent of the first Dominion Experimental Farm in Western Canada.

—*M. J. Ellis Photo.*

Samuel Larcombe of Birtle, Man., a Manitoba Wheat King.

Dr. W. P. Thompson who was made Companion of the Order of Canada in 1968, founded a plant-breeding program which produced suitable rust-resistant varieties of wheat.

Plate 1

—*Archives of Saskatchewan Photo.*

Dr. Charles Saunders, originator of
Marquis wheat.

Henry Wise Wood, awarded the
C.M.G. in 1935 "for service to agriculture in Western Canada."

David and Mrs. Fife of Peterborough, Ont., originators of Red Fife wheat.

Plate 2

Seager Wheeler of Rosthern, Sask.,
five times world Wheat King.

A. J. McPhail, president of Sask.
Co-operative Wheat Producers Ltd.

Pioneer farmer breaking virgin sod on a prairie homestead with oxen.

Plate 3

A heavy steam engine breaking prairie sod with a twelve-bottom plow.

Making the last round of the field with an eight-bottom plow. The outfit was owned by C. L. Myrick of Davidson, Sask.

Plate 4

Cultivating the soil with ox power and horse power in 1906 on the farm of J. G. Millar, Craik, Sask.

Plate 5

Eight binders cutting a field of wheat south of Rosebud, Alta. In foreground individual sheaves of wheat can be seen while in the right background they have been gathered together and placed in stooks by stookers who followed the binders.

Plate 6

Threshing about 1907 on the Myrick farm near Davidson, Sask., with a Waterloo steamer. The steamer supplied motive power for the separator (at rear) which removed the wheat and blew the straw and chaff out at the rear eventually to build up large straw stacks.

Gasoline engines eventually replaced steamers and here threshing is being carried out in 1928 with an Avery gasoline powered outfit.

Plate 7

A typical western harvest scene in the 1920s showing stooks of wheat sheaves standing in the stubble in the foreground, threshing outfit and straw stack in the middle distance and a row of country grain elevators in the background.

After harvest was completed the straw stacks were often burned. The above sight was common in the 1920s.

Plate 8

—Alberta Government Photo.

A world championship sample of Chinook wheat grown at Beiseker, Alta.

Plate 9

Combines and truck operating during harvest in a typical prairie scene of the 1960s. The combine in lead is drawn by a crawler tractor, the next combine is an SP (self-propelled) type with its own motive power. The grain is harvested and the kernels collected in the hopper on the left side of the combine. Trucks come along side and the grain is transferred to them through the spout which looks somewhat like the head and neck of a bird.

—T. R. Melville-Ness Photo.

As harvesting techniques changed with development of new machinery the stook-filled field disappeared and long rows of grain lying in swaths took its place. Above is a scene typical of the 1950s in the parkland area of the Prairies.

Plate 10

If there is storage room in the country elevator the farmer will sometimes haul his wheat directly to it from the field. If not he often stores it on his farm. Above a farmer has filled his metal storage bins (background) and is piling wheat on the ground.

This farmer has hauled his wheat by truck directly to the elevator where he is dumping it. As the grain flows out the elevator agent inspects it or grades it as basis for payment. If he doesn't agree with the agent's grading the farmer can appeal his case and have the Board of Grain Commissioners make final judgement.

Plate 11

The nature of the industry leaves its mark on the countryside and wheat fields give the land the appearance of a patchwork quilt. The fields above betray the strip-farming technique of growing grain on one long strip of land while allowing the strip next to it to lie fallow, to be seeded the following year.

Plate 12

From country elevators the wheat is loaded into boxcars which are collected and grow into long freight trains on their way to the terminal elevators either at inland water ports or saltwater ports on the coast. Here a Canadian Pacific train hauls wheat through the Sawbuck Range alongside the Bow River in the Rocky Mountains on the way to the Pacific coast.

Plate 13

—*T. R. Melville-Ness Photo.*

At the terminal elevators the boxcars are emptied and the grain stored for shipment in lakeboats at inland ports or in sea-going vessels bound for foreign ports at saltwater ports. Above grain is delivered to the holds of a lakeboat through spouts at a Saskatchewan Wheat Pool terminal elevator at the Lakehead (Fort William, Port Arthur, Ont. on Lake Superior).

Plate 14

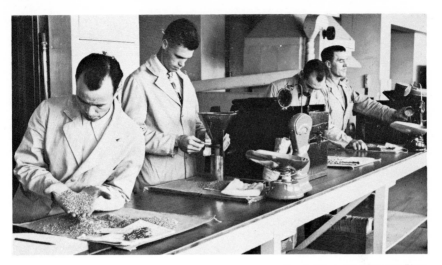

—*Board of Grain Commissioners Photo.*

Canada is jealous of the international reputation for high quality her wheat has won. An important factor in maintaining high standards is the manner in which the Board of Grain Commissioners carries out its inspection and research responsibilities. One of the research laboratories is seen above.

High quality wheat reaches the sales shelves of the world after being ground into the world's best baking flour in flour mills. Much is ground in Canada both for domestic use and for export but most wheat is exported in kernel form to be ground into flour at flour mills in foreign countries. Above flour is being bagged for sale.

Plate 15

— *Bakery Food Foundation of Canada Photo.*

The end result of the whole operation is the production of the finest bread in the world. At this stage the harvest of wheat actually becomes the harvest of bread.

Plate 16

꒰ ꒱

CHAPTER XVII

FIRST LINKS IN A CHAIN OF CHAMPIONSHIPS

꒰ ꒱

By qualifying for the World Wheat Crown in 1893, Rev. John Gough Brick forged the first link in what was to become a long chain of championships for Canada. His success at that time seemed strange and almost incomprehensible. Nobody expected the high honor to be won by a Canadian, regardless of where he might be growing grain. To compound the wonder of it all, the winning sample was from faraway Peace River and its grower was none other than an Anglican parson.

Skeptics inferred an element of accident, but nevertheless, the significance was not to be taken lightly. Brick, a young Englishman with a fancy for the frontier, was first of all a churchman, but when he established a mission at Shaftsbury on the north side of Peace River—between Dunvegin and Peace River Crossing—he insisted upon a farm as a companion enterprise.

To move breeding stock and farm equipment from Calgary, the nearest point on the railway in 1888, was a major operation. Brick lacked neither energy nor determination. So it was that Red Fife seed was carted over the long trails and trans-shipped by riverboat and canoe to Shaftsbury for the test on northern bush soil. For the spring planting in 1892, Brick had one bushel of high grade seed and for the next spring, he had seventy-two bushels.

Harvesting entailed heavy work because the entire crop had to be cut by sickle or scythe and threshed on the floor of the church by means of a flail. The final act of threshing consisted of tossing forkfuls of the beaten crop into the air and allowing northern breezes to carry away the straw and chaff and dust.

Both samples and yields were excellent. Somebody told Brick about a World's Fair at Chicago, and rather recklessly added a suggestion that the missionary should send a sample. Brick accepted the idea, reasoning that if his entry failed to win a prize, it would, at least, bring the name of Peace River to public attention. There was no such thing as hand picking at that time, but the west wind served well and the missionary's son, Allen, took the bag of show wheat over winter trails to Edmonton—a ten-day trip, with temperatures falling to 50 degrees below zero.

The wheat arrived at Chicago just in time for the judging. Then came the surprising announcement: "Red Fife Wheat From Peace River Wins Championship." Canadians were happy. The news did not reach the Reverend Mr. Brick at remote Peace River for two weeks.

After that notable triumph for Shaftsbury and the Church of England, there was a long period—eighteen years—during which Canadians did not figure in world championships. Modestly, they accepted an alleged superiority on the part of experienced growers in older parts of the continent. But the year of 1911 changed a few things.

The idea of exhibiting Marquis wheat in World's Fair competitions probably never entered the mind of its creator, Dr. Charles Saunders. He was a plant breeder, not an exhibitor. But exhibited by a skillful grower like Seager Wheeler, the new variety won its first world championship soon after being released and drew international attention to the Canadian Prairies. The biggest surprises were displayed right near home where men were asking: "Who is this Seager Wheeler?" and "Is this Marquis wheat all that good?"

In making Seager Wheeler a world champion fate was dealing mysteriously. If he had been one inch taller he would have been accepted by the British Navy and given no chance to grow wheat on the Canadian Prairies. Bitter at rejection by naval authority, he resolved to leave the Isle of Wight where he had grown up with people who drew their livelihood from the sea and had more interest in the Blackgang Pirates, with headquarters nearby, than with planting and harvesting of crops.

While still smarting from the disappointment of being rejected by the "blooming nyvey," he received a letter from an uncle, homesteading near Clark's Crossing, north of Saskatoon. It brought an idea: he would join the uncle in that far part. It was springtime, 1885, when the seventeen-year-old lad reached his uncle's place, 180 miles by trail from a railway.

His decision was to remain in the country and get a homestead for himself. He worked on railroad construction out of Moose Jaw for a while. Then, he saved some money, bought a wagon and team of oxen, and started north to his land.[35] His mother joined him to keep house in a lowly shelter made by placing poles in an upright position around a dugout on the riverbank.

Wheeler's first revenue came from gathering and selling buffalo bones —eight dollars per ton delivered. Bones paid for the groceries for most of the first two years. At the end of that time, the homesteader had some wheatland in production, but being less than satisfied with his homestead quarter, he made a change and bought a better place from the C.P.R. near Rosthern, Saskatchewan. On it the little man made a home, planted trees, and struggled to have his Red Fife wheat mature before the fall frosts came.

For one whose life and interests had been with ships and sailors, homesteading should have been completely foreign, but astonishingly enough he discovered an unsuspected fascination in the selection of crop plants and vegetables and flowers. The light from his kerosene lamp burned late at night as he hand-selected seeds. Neighbors, seeing him combing wheat fields for heads with special merit, said he was "odd." At one point he nearly lost his farm to a mortgage company; frozen wheat selling at twenty-three cents per bushel did extremely little to improve his security.

Conscious of the need for something earlier than Red Fife, Wheeler obtained Preston from Dr. William Saunders and saw it yield as high as sixty bushels per acre. But it was not the answer and Seager Wheeler admitted it.

At about this time, L. H. Newman, secretary of the Canadian Seed Growers' Association, visited Rosthern and spent some time with Wheeler. Together, they went into the fields, and Newman took time to explain experimental techniques, filling his pupil with resolve to become an expert in crop improvement.

During field exploration in 1910 Wheeler came upon a single head, obviously superior to plants around it. This head, with early maturity in its favor, was threshed separately and multiplied to give Wheeler the variety known as Red Bobs. From another selection he obtained the variety Kitchener which won some high honors, including the sweepstakes at the International Exposition at El Paso, Texas, in 1916.

It was the championship of 1911 that brought the clearest sounds of praise for Marquis wheat and the expanding Canadian wheat industry. Somebody who knew Seager Wheeler's skill with plants sent him a small sample of the new Marquis almost as soon as it was approved for distribution. It fulfilled expectations, and Seager Wheeler had enough seed for most of his planting in the spring of 1911. With almost parental devotion he watched tender shoots break through the soil, then stool, head, and ripen. Growth was about as high as Wheeler's head, and the little man knew what it was to become lost in wheat as he walked to remove weeds; it was like being lost in the woods. At threshing time he had the satisfaction of seeing golden grain pouring from the threshing machine spout, plump, clean, heavy, red, and hard. It was the best wheat he had ever seen and neighbors examining it in double handfuls said it should be sent to the Provincial Seed Fair at Regina. Cleaning a bushel or two to make it look its best was a labor of love, but he remained reluctant about entering a competition. Neighborly coaxing triumphed, however, and the Wheeler entry went forward to Regina, there to win the provincial championship.

After that, Wheeler did not have to be coaxed. Later in the year a sample of his Marquis wheat was on its way to the New York Land Show. It seemed like a bold adventure, but it was in line with the conviction of people like Sir Thomas Shaughnessy of the C.P.R. who believed a Canadian entry had a chance of winning.

James J. Hill of Great Northern Railway offered a gold cup valued at $1,000 for the best exhibit of wheat grown in the United States. Sir Thomas chided his railway counterpart, hoping the competition would be open to Canadian exhibitors as well as to those in the United States. Hill, adamant, repeated sternly: "Grown in the United States."

"All right," Sir Thomas replied, "if you won't do it, my company will give $1,000 in gold to the exhibitor of the best hard spring wheat, grown anywhere in the world. We'll see what happens."

The Shaughnessy hunch was sound, and days later the news was flashed across the country: "Man From Rosthern, Saskatchewan, Wins World Wheat Championship For Canada." People in the homestead country were exuberant in their joy while those in more distant parts took out maps to determine the location of that place called Rosthern.

A short time after the New York Show, Calgary was the scene of a banquet at which a railway executive presented Seager Wheeler with $1,000 in gold coins. With twinkles in his eyes, the man from Rosthern then passed the money back to the railway official, saying: "Thank you for the thousand dollars. Now, you take it as the final payment on my farm which I bought from the C.P.R."

It was the first major showring success for Marquis, as it was for Wheeler, but it was not to be the last for either. Winning international championships began to resemble a habit. Five times Wheeler won the World Wheat Championship for Canada. After winning with Marquis in 1911, he repeated with the same variety in 1914 and 1915. In 1916 his crop was destroyed by hail, but he won the International Sweepstakes with Kitchener wheat carried over from the previous year. Then, for the fifth time, he won the supreme honor in 1918, this time with Red Bobs. It was in the latter year, too, that Queen's University at Kingston, Ontario, recognized his great record with wheat and conferred upon him the honorary degree, Doctor of Laws.

While working skillfully with wheat and other cereals, forage crops and potatoes and fruits received his attention. Nor did Dr. Seager Wheeler forget a good husbandman's responsibility to the soil.

"The soil," said he, "is ours to make or mar and we should aim to leave it, when the time comes to pass it on to a future generation, practically in as good or better condition than when it first came under our hand."

The winning of international championships for wheat did, indeed, begin to resemble a habit in the West. In the fifty-four contests from 1911 to 1968, western Canadian growers claimed the high honor forty-eight times. Proof of quality could scarcely be more convincing!

CHAPTER XVIII

⌒☙⌒

COPING WITH THE WEATHER

⌒☙⌒

Growers might curse western weather, but nobody in homestead country was ready to surrender to it without a struggle. The hope was to outguess it in its spells of cussedness. Early fall frosts bringing ruination to promising stands of Red Fife and other grains challenged frontier imagination. Some farmers tried bonfires and smudges in the fields, hoping to keep late August and early September night temperatures from reaching the freezing point. As the influence did not extend far from the fire, crop growers knew they had to look elsewhere for relief. The best benefit, of course, came from that plant breeder's masterpiece, early-maturing Marquis wheat, the adoption of which meant more grain in stooks and bins when night temperatures took their autumn plunge.

Dealing with drought was more difficult. Wheat possessed some added natural drought resistance; in years of low rainfall, it could be expected to outyield oats and barley in dry matter per acre. However, to ensure a worth-while return in years when precipitation fell much below twelve or fourteen inches, as it did too often in southwestern Saskatchewan and southeastern Alberta, special measures were needed.

Man-made attempts to obtain extra rain, like those undertaken by the celebrated Charlie Hatfield[36] at Medicine Hat in 1921, produced more amusement than moisture. Farmers concluded that if they were to over-come Nature's failure to be generous with precipitation, they would have to practice dry farming methods with regular summerfallowing, or bring irrigation water to the thirsty fields.

By 1912 there was clear evidence of a new determination to beat the drought. Lethbridge, in that year, made agricultural history by acting as the host city for the Seventh Annual International Dry Farming Congress. For local people, it was like a World's Fair and many Lethbridge buildings were treated to exterior paint for the first time. Opened officially on

October 21, 1912, by Alberta's Lieutenant-Governor Bulyea, the event was an overwhelming success, except for the ironic inconvenience of heavy rains while dry farming delegates gave their attention to problems of aridity. At one point in the proceedings, a visiting speaker found himself unable to talk loudly enough to overcome the noise of rain falling heavily upon the roof.

But the dry farming exhibits were numerous and attendance far exceeded expectations. Accorded the privilege of conducting the World Wheat Championship Competitions for the year, local people had the added pleasure of seeing Henry Holmes, from nearby Raymond, win the supreme honor—the second time in two years for a Canadian grower to qualify for the coveted Wheat Crown. Again the winning wheat was Marquis.

At that time irrigation ditches were becoming more numerous, especially in southern Alberta where, because of water resources in high mountain streams, the opportunities far exceeded those existing in neighboring provinces eastward.

Irrigation in its simplest form was practiced in the Old World for thousands of years. Settlers along the Red and Assiniboine Rivers in Manitoba saw no particular need for it, but homesteaders and squatters far to the west had many reminders of the possible advantages. The practice was introduced to the Canadian West in 1878 when Irish-born John Glenn, squatting a few miles south of Fort Calgary, directed water from Fish Creek to irrigate a twenty-acre flat, beside the present-day Number 2 Highway at Midnapore.

A succession of dry years in the eighties and early nineties led to passage of the North West Irrigation Act of 1894. It provided that all water except subterranean or percolating water was vested in the Crown. Hence, the diversion or impounding of any stream water, except by license, was forbidden.

The next decade saw some large irrigation operations being started. The Macleod Irrigation Company was the first to receive a Dominion charter. The Galt Railway Company was irrigating in 1897 and by 1898, slightly more than 100,000 acres in what is now southern Alberta were being served by irrigation canals.

The earliest irrigation projects were undertaken by individual farmers and ranchers, but these were followed quickly by corporation, government, and co-operative schemes on the grander scale.

The leading promoter during the early period was William Pearce, author of the still controversial William Pearce Scheme. The vigorous and imaginative Mr. Pearce would have taken water from the North Saskatchewan, Clearwater and Red Deer Rivers and stored it in Sullivan Lake to irrigate over a million acres in central Alberta and west central Saskatchewan.

Most prominent among private corporations was the Canadian Pacific Railway. Ultimate operations made the railway company the continent's leader in irrigation. After being granted land subsidies, consisting of odd-numbered sections for twenty-four miles on both sides of the main line, the company exchanged parts of its holdings for unbroken blocks suitable for irrigation development, chiefly between Medicine Hat and Calgary. Three large areas were developed, the Western Irrigation District, a short distance east of Calgary; the Eastern Irrigation, lying a hundred miles or more east of Calgary; the Alberta Railway and Irrigation property, on the southeast side of Lethbridge. Water for the Western District was taken from the Bow River, not far below Calgary, and for the Eastern District from the same river, where a dam was built near Bassano.

The Railway Company made big investments, hoping to recover reward from expanded railroad traffic resulting from increased productivity. Development was reaching a peak about the time Seager Wheeler won his first international wheat championship, and Henry Holmes showed the world's best at Lethbridge.

One big scheme after another was promoted, like the Canada Land and Irrigation Company which, with English capital, embarked upon an extensive program in southern Alberta just before the years of World War I. The motivation was "wheat and other fruits of the soil" to be grown with new dependability. But, like some other companies, the Canada Land and Irrigation Company encountered losses and achieved only a part of its ambitious objective.

The Lethbridge Northern became a well-known community co-operative, generally northeast of Lethbridge, taking water from the Oldman River. The Southern Alberta Land Company, with J. D. McGregor as Managing Director, was formed in 1909 and took water from the Bow River for storage in the Lake McGregor Reservoir. Then came the Canada Wheat Lands, Limited, in 1911, securing an option on 64,000 acres from Southern Alberta Land Company, about two-thirds of which were to be irrigated. Twelve thousand acres were broken in 1911 and 13,000 in 1912. Water was to be delivered in 1914. Ditches were constructed, but with the outbreak of war, Southern Alberta Land Company operations were suspended. Although the Company was reorganized, some of the ditches never did carry water.

After two and one-half decades of direct participation, the Canadian Pacific Railway Company changed its irrigation policy. In 1935 it handed over to the District's water users, the entire Eastern Irrigation operation, including 1,500,000 acres of land, of which 60,000 acres were under irrigation. Given, also, was cash amounting to $300,000. A few years later, in 1941, the Western District operation was transferred to those who were using its water. For all parties concerned they were transactions of extreme importance, and as farmer-owned enterprises, both systems flourished.

With most of the West's irrigation water originating in the Rocky Mountains it was to be expected that Alberta would take the lead in development programs. Eight mountain streams combine to form the South Saskatchewan River, and two to form the North Saskatchewan. With help from governments and the Prairie Farm Rehabilitation Act (1935)—the foremost promoter of irrigation in recent years—the province of Saskatchewan gained potential relief for dry soils with the completion of the South Saskatchewan River Dam in 1967. Farmers close to the huge dam were slow in their acceptance of the irrigation principle, but the country won the capacity to furnish water for an additional half-million acres of Palliser Triangle land.

True, irrigation farmers have diversified more than dry land operators, but retaining an affection for wheat, many of them have continued to grow it.

CHAPTER XIX

꧁ ☯ ꧂

THE BANNER YEAR 1915

꧁ ☯ ꧂

Flaming strawpiles lit up night skies in the fall of 1915 as never before—and never since. It was not that burning occurred as a new practice; the bigger stacks and more numerous fires were simply a reflection of the bumper crop across the country.

Wheat straw was low in feeding value and the West did not have enough cattle to eat the large amounts blown into piles. Stacks of oat straw were spared rather often for feed and an occasional stack of wheat straw was kept for stable bedding, but most piles were fired on the first night after threshing outfits pulled away. On almost any September night in 1915 residents in wheat country could have counted a dozen or more spectacular blazes lighting the horizons as if by fireworks.

More important than the autumn display of burning was the crop year which produced the straw. For many years western farmers reserved their choicest superlatives for 1915. Like the year of the Klondike Gold Rush or the Chicago Fire, 1915 was a year to remember. It was the "Year of the Big Crop." If more had been needed to confirm the West as wheat country, the crop response of that year furnished it.

It was also a troubled and bloody time, with the echo of World War I cannon fire being heard around the globe. Early in the year, German submarines were launched upon a blockade of Britain, and food production and delivery became matters of extreme concern to the Allies. Wheat prices at Chicago reached the highest point since 1898. Plantings in Manitoba, Saskatchewan and Alberta were increased to 13,868,000 acres, biggest acreage ever for the new country. The resulting crop, of record size, appeared as one of Nature's thoughtful provisions for people in distress.

Moreover, there was a bit of drama about the production of the big crop. Spring prospects were clearly unfavorable because of dry soil. Reserves of moisture in most areas were far below average, and some growers wondered if they were throwing seed away by planting it in soils too dry to ensure germination. Rainfall in the previous autumn was less than normal and winter snowfall was light. At Calgary precipitation totalled only 0.4 inches in January, 0.22 inches in February and 0.66 inches in March. Farmers had good reason to be pessimistic about crop prospects, although further experience on western soil was to demonstrate clearly the folly of ever judging crops until grain is in the bins.

Even total precipitation for the entire twelve months of 1915 was less than average in many parts of the country. Regina showed only 9.9 inches for the year, while Saskatoon had 10.48 inches, and Prince Albert, 11.62 inches. The secret of the year's crop success lay in the fact that rains fell precisely when needed in the growing season. Rainfall for April, May, June and July at Prince Albert amounted to 7.34 inches or almost two-thirds of the year's total moisture. Likewise, rainfall in the same four growing months at Swift Current, Regina, Saskatoon, Moose Jaw and Grenfell represented well over half of the precipitation for the whole year.

At any rate, prairie fields which were dry and dusty at seeding time responded quickly to timely rains and took on the character of abundance. Harvesting conditions were favorable except for shortage of help because many young men had left the farms for army service. When crop recovery was complete, however, production for the three Midwestern provinces stood at 360,000,000 bushels, an unprecedented yield average of 26 bushels per acre. The country had to wait for another thirty-seven years before experiencing such a high yield average again.

Western Canada's wheat production had exceeded 100,000,000 bushels for the first time in 1906. Five years later, it passed the 200,000,000 bushel mark. Now, in 1915, with output exceeding 300,000,000 bushels, Canada claimed a place of prominence among world leaders and exporters of wheat.

Most of Canada's wheat of 1915 was grown in Saskatchewan, which established it as the undisputed Wheat Province. The beginning of September marked the tenth anniversary of the creation of the two provinces, Saskatchewan and Alberta, but their people—most of whom were actively engaged in farming—were too busy recovering crop to stop for a celebration.

Not only was the crop of 1915 a big one, but most of what was grown that year was Marquis and of supremely high quality. When Seager Wheeler won the world championship for wheat for the third time late in that year, it seemed like the most fitting climax.

By 1915, about 450,000 homesteads had been taken in the West, and for many people struggling to gain title and independence, the crop of that year gave them their first or best cash return. Leaders in other industries were forced to acknowledge the impact of wheat upon the economy across the entire country. Winnipeg saw more than 1,000 cars of grain per day come in from the west and move on eastward throughout a big part of the 1915-16 crop year.

CHAPTER XX

❦

THRESHING WITH STEAM

❦

Autumn days in wheat country, 1915, left no doubt about the dominant source of power for belt work. Threshing power meant steam engines, big, awkward and heavy enough to wreck any bridge in the municipality unless precautions were taken to reinforce the structure with extra planks or timbers.

But the big steamers were majestic, and in spite of hard work which went with threshing, they brought a fascination to the harvest operations. Long after they were replaced by more modern equipment in western wheat fields, there remained those men with strong sentiment and affection for steam threshing, men who could overcome a springtime urge to set a hen or go fishing easier than banish the autumn longing to hear the blasts from a steam whistle, pitch sheaves until muscles ached, eat big meals of farm fare, chew a little tobacco, watch golden grain come down the spout, and retire at night to a badly ventilated bedroom on wheels. It was the accepted way for many years, and a big itinerant outfit, getting a thirty-to fifty-day run, might do the threshing for a dozen or more farmers.

Anybody who worked as a member of a threshing "gang" in those years, guarded the memory of the problems and difficulties. The pioneer thresherman would remember when the big tractor, weighing more than ten tons, crashed through a bridge or bogged down in wet ground and required the help of sixteen horses to get it out. He could tell of a "long move" of from four to six miles, requiring all night on the trail with one man carrying a lantern and walking ahead in the hope of avoiding damp and soft ground.

Alexander MacEwan, who pioneered at Brandon, had the first big steam tractor in that part, also what he believed to be the first big separator equipped with self-feeder and wind-stacker west of Portage la Prairie. The outfit, costing the nigh-crippling sum of $4,000, consisted of a Minneapolis tractor and a 42-60 separator. The engine was of the return-flue type with smoke funnel at the rear end.

In its first autumn that big outfit operated for sixty days, threshing for twenty farmers in the district, and leaving behind it a string of broken bridges, including Brandon's Eighteenth Street Bridge across the Assiniboine River. Repairing bridges, especially the big ones, proved costly, and thereafter when the river had to be crossed, the steamer and separator were loaded on a flatcar and moved by railroad.

With such an outfit, of course, there was the equivalent of a small army of men and horses. Two pitchers accompanied each of eight stook wagons, intended to provide for four men pitching into the feeder continuously. In addition to the sixteen men with stook wagons, there were four or five teamsters hauling away the threshed grain, also the engineer, fireman, separator man, straw man, tank man and finally, that hardy soul who seemed obliged to live through the threshing season with only a little food and no sleep—the boss. This was the crew, which proved on at least one occasion that it could thresh 1,000 bushels of wheat in three hours.

That separator represented the climax to a hundred years of improvement upon the invention of the Scottish mechanic, Andrew Meikle,[37] but it did not operate without failures and delays. There was a repair job nearly every night, sometimes taking all night. The primitive self-feeder, which was intended to remove much of the hardship from threshing, gave trouble and, after the first year, was removed to allow feeding to continue by hand. Thereafter, four men pitched sheaves from loads to the tables, while two men cut bands and two others fed the cut sheaves into the jaws of the threshing cylinder. Altogether, eight men worked at the feeder end of the machine.

Better feeders and better separators made their appearance, but that particular steam tractor gave long service in the farming community. Ultimately, it was dismantled and its huge drive wheels were converted to paddle wheels for a steamboat to operate on the Assiniboine River.

Getting and holding a good threshing crew was often a difficult matter. Frequently the teamsters were neighbors working to help defray the cost of threshing their own crops; sometimes they were homesteaders with no crop of their own; and occasionally they were the hard-working, hard-drinking men who worked in lumber camps in winter and came to the farming districts at harvest time. Anyway, they received $1.50 a day.

In later years Harvesters' Excursions were instituted, and many young men from eastern Canada obtained their first glimpses of the Prairies in this way. Some remained to farm; others found the sheaves too heavy or the alkali water too terrible and went home with the least possible delay.

If the outfit had a leading man or hero, the honor would rest with the engineer. He held a certificate or diploma to prove his qualifications and he commanded the biggest wages and by far the biggest share of attention. If he was fortunate in having an outfit in good state of repair, he was not particularly busy. He was the one man who worked by his wits rather than his muscles, and as he stood on the great drive wheel of the tractor and surveyed operations with the air of a Field Marshal watching a military operation, young and ambitious spectators were filled with hope of some-day achieving such a pinnacle of success. When he placed his hand on the throttle and the mighty wheels responded, his smug satisfaction could not be concealed. It was the same when he pulled the cord to the whistle and human ears for miles around picked up the message; one long blast for quitting time; two long blasts to tell the tank man, pumping at some distant slough or creek, to hurry with water; three long blasts to remind teamsters with grain wagons that they would be needed quickly if the outfit was not to be held up for want of a place to deposit the wheat; a series of short toots was a warning to drivers of stook wagons that somebody had to make better time or the machine would be obliged to idle.

Nobody received sympathy, regardless of fatigue and blisters. But the one most deserving of sympathy was the fireman. The first to arise in the morning in order to have steam by daylight, he fired by pushing straw into the firebox almost continuously from about four in the morning until seven at night. It was not surprising that when firemen went to town on Saturday nights, they rather frequently failed to return for Monday mornings.

Then there was the old-time separator man, commanding the second highest wage. His job was not glamorous; it was dusty and noisy. He was expected to have untold knowledge about bearings and concaves and pulleys. In the art of lacing belts, he was a master. Such knowledge did not come from book learning but from years of dusty and greasy experience. For fully half of his time he seemed to be squirting lubricating oil into holes and crannies which nobody but himself knew existed.

An able separator man could mean much to the success of an outfit. His reputation was determined by the absence of delays, but weather could impose losses of time for which no human could be held respon-sible. Threshing after freeze-up or when snow covered the stooks, some-times inevitable, made life particularly unpleasant for the separator man. If bad weather lasted for more than three weeks, he was likely to come under observation for symptoms of madness.

Deserving of more admiration than they received were the farm women who fed those ravenous threshers. As soon as it was known that the crew was coming, the kitchen table was extended by ingenious means until the seating capacity reached the necessary fifteen, twenty or twenty-five places. Great stocks of food were made ready, and farm women breathed earnest prayers for good weather and the shortest possible threshing time. It was not much wonder that thought of delay or breakdown struck terror to feminine hearts. Meals had to be provided as usual whether the weather was fit for threshing or not. The farm woman whose misfortune was to have threshers through a prolonged spell of wet weather, and who served 650 meals before the fields were clear, could have nothing but the most unpleasant memories of the big steam-driven outfits. The potato peeling involved, the cooking of beef, baking of bread, and washing of dishes would be more than enough to totally obscure any of the alleged romance connected with threshing at that time.

Workmen could appreciate a farm wife all the more when they had to move for threshing on premises where meals were prepared and served by a bachelor homesteader. Unless the man was unusually skillful as a housekeeper, he could expect some embarrassment from threshermen, who were not totally insensitive to unsanitary conditions. A Brandon bachelor farmer was noticeably insulted when a teamster had the temerity to wash out the endless, or more correctly, perpetual hand towel hanging on a roller, and when another undertook to empty the tea pot, discovering among the accumulations of time something which still had its fur in a fine state of preservation. That man's bachelor fare was so unpopular that the threshers worked long overtime one night—without extra pay—finishing by lantern light to avoid the necessity of eating another breakfast of his making.

Like members of a baseball team, each of the fifteen or twenty-five men and farm women working to complete the threshing had an essential part to play. To a large extent, threshing in 1915 was a co-operative undertaking, with the entire community participating. Wagons, racks, and horse teams were drawn from neighboring farms, which would be served by the same threshing outfit. Even dishes and pans were passed around from farm to farm until the season's work was finished.

But nothing seems more certain than change, and before the end of World War I the big and cumbersome steam engines as sources of farm power were being challenged and displaced. Gasoline tractors of large size had a short period of popularity, to be followed by tractors and threshers of small or medium size, and finally, by combines, some of them self-propelled. Indicative of the degree and rapidity of the changes was the experience of men who had used flails for the threshing of wheat grown on early Manitoba farms and who lived to see crops on the same land being harvested and threshed in a single operation by means of a modern combine.

In any case, the glory of the steam tractor and big threshing unit departed. Those slow-moving but lordly giants seen today as museum pieces are memories of a proud period in Canada's agricultural history.

CHAPTER XXI

∽☙∾

A SHIFT IN MARKETING METHODS

∾☙∽

Wartime stringency changed the whole shape of wheat marketing in Canada. Government controls and Board selling were introduced for war years, and for the years immediately after, as emergency and purely temporary measures, but as things turned out, the experiences were enough to influence selling methods for decades ahead.

Canada's marketing system had evolved gradually, changing and adapting like an animal organism adjusting to a new environment. Elevator companies and railroads enlarged to meet changing demands; the Winnipeg Grain Exchange, a voluntary organization created for the trade, by the trade, became a powerful supervisory body. More than merely a local institution, the Winnipeg Grain Exchange became a world leader, ranking with the corresponding exchanges at Liverpool and Chicago. For years, Chicago was the world's biggest dealer in grain "futures,"[38] and Winnipeg the biggest as a cash wheat market.

To ensure order and uniformity in selling the country's grain, some regulating authority was needed. Nobody would question the necessity. The Winnipeg Grain Exchange was the voice of men in the trade, who were prepared to furnish the required service. The Exchange did not escape farmer criticism, but it should be remembered that it was a pioneer body, and much of the service it provided in facilities and supervision to prevent dishonest practices was useful, even essential.

To growers in the wheat country, the biggest source of suspicion was futures trading, a Winnipeg Grain Exchange innovation of 1904. Perhaps it, too, served a useful purpose, removing some of the risk of falling prices facing dealers, millers, and exporters before they could obtain a return from their purchases. At one time, the risk appeared large enough to justify deductions of a few cents a bushel from payments made to growers.

Nevertheless, farmers took a dim view of gambling on the prices of their wheat after they had delivered it. If somebody in Winnipeg was getting rich from transactions in wheat, farmers were sure there was something wrong with the open market and its speculative trading feature. Whatever could be said for or against the system, instability of prices was clearly one of its shortcomings. Fluctuation might have suited men in the trade, but it did not suit the men on the land. Somehow, as prices rose and fell, growers generally sold at the wrong time, or so they said. Suspicion grew, and farmers wanted further safeguards.

Royal Commissions had not really condemned the established selling methods, but the Government was well aware of discontent in the prairie country and was prepared to provide more control over handling and grading. The Canada Grain Act passed the House of Commons and came into effect on April 1, 1912. It provided for the appointment of a Board of Grain Commissioners to supervise weighing, inspection, grading, and the general processes in handling of grains. It would license elevator owners and demand security bonds for the protection of elevator customers. It would fix fees which elevator operators could charge for storage and other services. The Board would be allowed to purchase or construct terminal elevators, but it had no authority to regulate or attempt to regulate prices. Executive offices for the Board would be in Winnipeg, a logical place for them.

Western farmers were grateful for the new safeguards; men in the Winnipeg Grain Exchange were grateful for the freedom to continue their operations as previously. With little delay, Board of Grain Commission members were appointed. Grading received immediate attention, and almost at once, Canada's grading system gained respect. Number One Manitoba Hard and Number One Manitoba Northern became hallmarks of quality around the world. When wheat was shipped overseas with the "Canadian Certificate Final" attached, buyers received it with confidence.

Farmers admitted improvement in marketing following the appointment of the Board. Complaints from the wheat country subsided for a few years or until World War I brought totally new circumstances. Wheat prices on world markets turned sharply upwards, as is usually the case when serious disruption threatens food supplies. Men who were sensitive to the rising cost of living wondered where wheat prices would stop. Growers who had long complained about low prices would have been quite willing to let supply and demand take their course, but people in government had other ideas.

Intervention was inescapable, and late in 1915, while many overseas countries were more eager than ever to obtain Canadian wheat, the

Government of Canada seized control of all wheat at the Head of the Lakes. A few months later, the British Government—still looking to Canada for most of its needs in wheat, in spite of the very great difficulty in ocean shipping—appointed a buying agency to handle all Canadian purchases.

The presence of such a committee in Winnipeg was, naturally, a blow to brokers and dealers whose business had long depended upon British sales.

A short time later, the British buying agency—called the Wheat Export Company—was given the task of purchasing for all the Allied countries in Europe.

Wheat prices continued to creep upward, touching $3.00 per bushel for May wheat at Winnipeg on May 11, 1917, and $3.43 per bushel at Chicago on the next day. The Canadian Government, anxious to protect both bread consumers and wheat growers against price extremes, found itself being drawn more and more into actual purchase and sale. Under the circumstances there seemed to be no justification for gambling in wheat. In order to suspend speculation in something which meant bread for hungry people, the futures market at Winnipeg was closed on May 3, 1917.

Canada and the United States faced roughly the same problems and took roughly the same action to meet them. South of the boundary, the Government set up the United States Grain Corporation, a monster monopoly to buy, sell, and distribute the country's wheat. There, as in Canada, trading in futures ended, and wheat marketing was removed completely from private enterprise. Prices were those fixed by the Corporation.

With exactly the same purpose, the Government of Canada, on June 11, 1917, created the Board of Grain Supervisors but gave it rather less authority than was given to the United States body. The primary functions of the Canadian Board were to ensure the best distribution of the precious wheat at home and abroad, and secondly, to fix wheat prices without becoming the monster buying agency. Thus, Board responsibility was regulation rather than actual purchase and sale.

The Board of Grain Supervisors consisted of eleven members and included representatives from the Board of Grain Commissioners, Winnipeg Grain Exchange, farm organizations, and labor bodies—also at least one person who was to speak essentially for the Canadian consumers.

In line with instructions, the Board of Grain Supervisors set prices for wheat and revised them as circumstances seemed to warrant. In its

first order, to apply August 1, 1917, the maximum price of wheat, basis
Number One Northern at Fort William, was $2.40 per bushel. The Board
then made it clear that all futures trading would remain, for the time
being, closed.

But this was not enough. In September, 1918, the Government of
Canada took the further step and gave the Board of Grain Supervisors
the control of all grain marketed, whether for domestic consumption or
export. Food had become about as important as munitions, and it was
imperative that all available supplies be directed to the places where need
was greatest. Canadian millers, exporters, overseas purchasing agents, and
all who wanted wheat were obliged, thereafter, to deal with the Board.

A couple of months later, World War I ended, but it made no immediate difference to wheat marketing problems. The difficulty of distribution and need for price control did not disappear. Famine still
threatened in Europe, and reserves of world wheat were low. The Board
of Grain Supervisors was to be disbanded. Worried farmers wondered what
would follow if marketing were allowed to return to its former pattern.
With world conditions as they were, speculators would have "field days."

It suited the grain trade to let marketing revert to its old ways but
it did not suit the growers, especially when it was known that other countries, including the United States, had fixed prices for the 1919 crop.
Farmers, through the Canadian Council of Agriculture, appealed to the
Government for the establishment of a national pool or Wheat Board
with complete control of sales. There were people who objected
strenuously to the compulsory feature of a national pool, but the request
was granted and the first Canadian Wheat Board was set up to market
the crop of 1919.

The Grain Exchange was still closed and the Board announced an
initial price of $2.15 per bushel. It was a new experience for most farmers
to receive participation certificates, entitling them to a share in any
surplus returns when the Board had sold the year's wheat. They did not
know what to make of it, but there was a pleasant surprise for them in
October, 1920, when the Wheat Board made its final payment on the
1919 crop—an additional forty-eight cents per bushel. Skeptics quickly
became friends of the Wheat Board principle.

But the Government of the day had very little enthusiasm for Board
marketing and was anxious to get out of the wheat business. Actually, the
Wheat Board's life was brief; it ended in 1920 and the country returned
to open marketing. Farmers were unhappy. Prices dropped—as they might
have been expected to do anyway in a postwar period. Rightly or wrongly,

farmers reasoned that "prices would have been better if we had a Board."

Although the western crops of 1921 and 1922 were fairly good, returns seemed inadequate. Farm debts increased rapidly; men on the land were more critical than ever of the open market and Grain Exchange. They wanted another Wheat Board—or something of the kind.

CHAPTER XXII

⌘

THE WHEAT POOLS

⌘

Open trading was resumed on the Winnipeg Grain Exchange, August 18, 1920. Wheat prices remained strong for a brief period; then, from a peak of $2.85 per bushel in September, 1920, began a slow and sickening decline to less than a dollar a bushel late in 1923.

Farmers, watching prices fall, thought and talked longingly about the Wheat Board of 1919-20. Whether such a body had actually resulted in higher prices than would have prevailed with the open market was debatable, but it served to remove the day-to-day price fluctuations which appeared more objectionable when wheat was selling close to one dollar per bushel than when it was still near the two dollar mark. Nor could men on the land forget that windfall of forty-eight cents, final bushel payment on the 1919 crop, marketed through the Board.

The experiences of war years and the two years following made one point very clear: There was, indeed, an alternative to speculative marketing. Farmers clamored for another Wheat Board. When it was denied, they were in a mood for bold action. Why not a giant wheat marketing co-operative, they asked, a strictly do-it-yourself operation embracing the pooling feature of a Wheat Board? Even in 1922, the leaders in one farm organization were proposing a voluntary pool for wheat.

Men on the land were not strangers to co-operation. They might not know the technicalities laid down by English weavers at Rochdale,[39] but they knew very well the practical benefits of working together at roundup or threshing season, when a sick neighbor needed help, or a community hall had to be built. Regardless of how individualistic the pioneers might be, they were ever ready to help each other when need arose.

Organized co-operatives, however, were something quite different. The exact time when they appeared in Canada is not clear. The earliest may have been in Nova Scotia where one is thought to have been set up about

1765. There is clearer evidence of Stellarton coal miners having their own store in the year 1861, also of a mutual fire insurance organization in the Province of Quebec, starting in 1852. A consumer co-operative was started at Winnipeg about 1885, and for some years after 1896, the Federal Government assisted in organizing co-operative creameries across the West. Reference has been made to the founding in 1901 of the Territorial Grain Growers' Association under the leadership of W. R. Motherwell and John Millar.

Then came the co-operative elevators. The Government of Manitoba was persuaded to go in for publicly-owned elevators and between 1910 and 1912, acquired about 170 of them. Later, these were sold to the Grain Growers' Grain Company.

Saskatchewan, in 1910, named a commission to study all aspects of grain marketing, and in line with recommendations, the Saskatchewan Co-operative Elevator Company was formed in the following years. The Provincial Government, in this case, loaned most of the money needed to build, but control of the elevators rested with the farmers.

The neighboring province had the Alberta Farmers' Co-operative Elevator Company, organized in 1913. Here again, the Government loaned 85 per cent of building costs. Soon after that, the Alberta Farmers' Co-operative Elevator Company was taken over by the Grain Growers' Grain Company, but the Saskatchewan Co-op continued until bought out by the Saskatchewan Wheat Pool in 1925.

Farmer-owned elevators furnished a good exercise in working together. Then came the most exciting chapter in the history of co-operation in Canada—or elsewhere—the organization of the western Wheat Pools. When, in the summer of 1923, all hope of obtaining a Government Wheat Board seemed to have vanished, leaders talked about acting for themselves. Supporting the self-help principle were leaders of various farm organizations, including the United Farmers of Alberta of which Henry Wise Wood was the able president. This man—with unusual gifts of leadership and perception and long the most influential individual in Canadian farm circles—moved from his native state of Missouri to the new province of Alberta in 1905. When the Alberta Farmers' Association and Society of Equity amalgamated to form the United Farmers of Alberta in 1909, farmer Wood became an active member. By 1916, he was the U.F.A. president and commanding an ever greater respect. Having been appointed to the Board of Grain Supervisors in 1917 and the Canadian Wheat Board in 1919, he had every opportunity to understand the grain marketing problems. He might have been Federal Minister of

Agriculture in the Union Government,[40] just as he could have been Premier of Alberta in 1921, but he chose to stay with his farm organization.

Looking and acting like a professor of philosophy or economics, he agreed that the time had come for action. The *Edmonton Journal* and *Calgary Herald* publishers invited Aaron Sapiro[41] to come from California to tell Canadians about successes with producer co-operatives in that state. Sapiro electrified his prairie audiences and filled farmers with determination to get along with organization. "Stop dumping and start merchandising," he proclaimed convincingly.

It was late in the season, and wheat fields were getting ripe. Should organization be attempted so late in the crop year or should advocates of pooling restrain their enthusiasm for the time being, to make an early-season start in 1924? Farm leaders were divided on the matter of timing. With Aaron Sapiro nodding approval, however, the decision was to undertake a crash-type campaign for grower support in the form of promises to deliver wheat for a contract period of five years.

Enthusiasm was rampant nearly everywhere except around the Winnipeg Grain Exchange. From August 20, when the sign-up campaign started, some farmers were so busy canvassing for contracts that they forgot or neglected their own harvests.

The object was to obtain contracts covering 50 per cent of Alberta's wheat acreage by September 5. On that date, 26,211 farmers had committed the wheat from 2,558,095 acres to pool marketing. It represented about 45 per cent of the provincial total acreage—a little less than the declared objective—but those directing the program decided to go ahead anyway. Inasmuch as the 50 per cent objective had not been reached, growers had the privilege, for two weeks, of withdrawing their contracts but less than 5 per cent of those signing showed any change of mind. A late start and other handicaps notwithstanding, the Alberta Wheat Pool succeeded in marketing 34,000,000 bushels from the 1923 crop. The year's price was $1.01 per bushel, basis Number One Northern, Fort William. Cost of handling was reported to be one-half cent per bushel but, best of all, farmers liked the price stability their co-operative operation brought to them.

Saskatchewan growers attempted to secure five-year delivery contracts covering six million acres in a twelve-day campaign, but failed to reach the goal and decided to defer until the next year. Likewise, in Manitoba, where Grain Trade opposition was most evident, the acreage desired was not obtained and the decision was to postpone further thought of implementing such a scheme until the next year.

Saskatchewan's counterpart to Henry Wise Wood was James Alexander McPhail, a forty-year-old bachelor farmer from Elfros. Having come west from Bruce County as a boy in 1899, he knew about pioneer struggles. His father died from tuberculosis one year after coming to the Prairies, and very soon after, his mother died. Schooling was limited, but McPhail was a student by nature. He was also a very determined man and in 1921, when Farmer candidates won the provincial election in Alberta, and the Prairie Provinces sent thirty-nine Progressive members of parliament to Ottawa, McPhail was proclaiming for co-operative marketing.

Although the Saskatchewan and Manitoba supporters were obliged to be nothing more than spectators in the first year of Alberta Wheat Pool operation, they were determined to carry their plan to fulfillment in 1924. Starting early in the season, Saskatchewan had very little difficulty in gaining acreage objectives. On June 16, Saskatchewan's McPhail wrote in his diary: "Wheat Pool over the top today."

As of that date, 46,509 Saskatchewan farmers had signed contracts, accounting for 50 per cent of the wheat acreage of the province. Days later, on July 25, McPhail was named to become the first president of the Saskatchewan Wheat Pool.

Manitoba, also, repeated the drive for members and acreage in 1924. Henry Wise Wood visited the province, addressing meetings and helping to promote the proposed Pool. With the Winnipeg influence, Manitoba presented more difficulties than either Saskatchewan or Alberta, and the contracted acreage was less than canvassers set out to get. But Manitoba workers were unshaken and went ahead with organization.

In July of that year, representatives of the three Provincial Pools met to discuss and form a Central Selling Agency, to be called, more correctly, the Co-operative Wheat Producers Limited. Saskatchewan's McPhail became chairman of the inter-provincial body—a position he retained until his death in 1931. Alberta's Wood was named to the office of vice-chairman and Manitoba's C. H. Burnell was elected secretary. Regardless of the organization's name, it was the biggest producer co-operative of its kind in the world.

The farmers were now in business—big business—and leaders like Henry Wise Wood, meditating philosophically with straight-stemmed pipe in one hand and a blackened match in the other, were sure they were right. Elevators were acquired, and most farmers liked the pooling principle and liked those final payments which seemed to represent the last cent it was possible to obtain from grains sold. Memberships increased to 140,000 in the three provinces, a total which was backed by no less than 15,000,000 acres.

That first contract period ended with a total of almost 1,000,000,000 bushels of grain marketed and cash turnover exceeding $1,000,000,000. In addition, there were some millions of dollars returned to farmers as patronage dividends from elevator operations.

While anti-Pool propaganda was more abundant than ever, a new sign-up campaign was undertaken in 1928 and by the end of October, there was positive proof of farmer approval. In Saskatchewan, it came in the form of 77,404 new contracts, representing 10,735,000 acres. It looked like an expression of faith.

But there were troubled times ahead.

CHAPTER XXIII

WHEAT POOLS IN TROUBLE

It had been Pool policy to make moderate initial payments when wheat was delivered, then interim payments part way through the year and final payments when the year's operations were concluded. Members liked the arrangement. Regardless of what critics said, there was some advantage in having crop income spread over the year.

The working plan was fine, at least until the economic "roof" seemed to be falling in at New York and elsewhere in October, 1929. The memorable market collapse meant financial disaster for many investors and institutions and looked like a deathblow to the Wheat Pools. Enemies of co-operative marketing, chuckling at the sudden turn of events, expected the Wheat Pools to disappear, never to return.

There had been a big prairie crop in 1928—some 545,000,000 bushels of wheat—although grades suffered on account of frost. It was the first time in Canadian history for production to exceed 500,000,000 bushels, and exports placed the country in a foremost position among world suppliers. The Pools, acting for their 150,000 members, handled almost half of the huge crop. It was big business; critics said it was dangerously big for men lacking in marketing experience.

In handling that big crop, the initial Pool payment was eight-five cents and later payments brought the total to about $1.20, basis Number One Northern, Fort William. Officials could show how they had effected savings in the cost of handling grain and the net result seemed quite satisfactory. The record of five or six successful years brought reasons for pride, but some leaders in the Pool movement believed they could show an even better performance if they had control of the entire wheat crop.

Aaron Sapiro gave the impression that he might be available for a well-paid managerial position with the Pools. He advocated the adoption of 100 per cent compulsory Pool and got strong support from L. C. Brouillette, vice-president of the Saskatchewan Wheat Pool. Just as convincing were Alberta's Henry Wise Wood and Saskatchewan's A. J. McPhail, both strongly opposed to the principle of compulsion. Great bitterness was generated over the issue even before the shock from market collapse struck the wheat country.

Regardless of domestic controversy, Pool officials stood on a record of successes and faced the marketing tasks of a new year with quiet confidence—perhaps more confidence than circumstances of the time really warranted. The initial payment, as announced, would be $1.00 per bushel. Wheat at Winnipeg was trading at around $1.50 per bushel, and even the bankers loaning money to finance the year's operations failed to see danger in the $1.00 initial payment.

Perhaps all concerned missed warning signals they should have seen. The world wheat situation was changing and not in the producer's favor. The Pools, themselves, had a carry-over of wheat from the 1928 crop and the world surplus was distinctly bigger than normal. As Pool enemies delighted to mention in later years, British grain merchants were noticeably antagonistic because of Pool selling methods. What the Liverpool men disliked most was the practice of withholding grain when prices declined.

Anyway, the month of October in that fateful year deserved to be called the Month of Bankruptcy. With the New York market setting the pace, commodity prices shot downward. Wheat tobogganed to the point at which the Pools could lose control of their grains. For Pool leaders, there were frustrations and sleepless nights.

When the price reached $1.15 per bushel—equal to the initial payment plus a 15 per cent margin—the bank creditors could have exercised their right to force sales in order to protect their equity. That crisis was averted when the three Provincial Governments—Alberta, Saskatchewan and Manitoba—following appeals from the Pools, guaranteed the banks against loss, and the Pools were thereby free to hold their stocks of wheat for the price recovery most people expected.

But prices did not recover; they went lower and did not stop at the initial price paid by the Pools. Wheat became hard to sell at any price. With much of the year's crop selling away below $1.00 per bushel, the Provincial Pools ended up with huge debts to their respective Provincial Governments, $12,500,000 in Saskatchewan, $5,500,000 in Alberta and $3,300,000 in Manitoba.

It was a gala day for Pool enemies in Winnipeg and elsewhere. The

Pools brought the trouble on themselves, they said, and, finding the total Pool indebtedness to Provincial Governments at about $22,000,000, they were sure none of it would be repaid. They called for liquidation. Some Liverpool voices joined in the accusing chorus, making it quite evident that the overseas merchants would be happy to see the end of Pool selling.

The criticisms voiced so freely at that time may or may not have been justified, but one thing was certain: The economic depression was not limited to any single commodity or any single area. It was worldwide and no fair-minded person would believe the Canadian Pools brought it on or had any significant effect upon it.

Nor did the troubles end in 1929. Most people looked for wheat prices to bounce back to some reasonable level. But they did not bounce back. Then there was the problem of borrowing money with which to finance the 1930 Pools. Again there were appeals to Provincial Governments, and again the banks were given guarantees against loss on loans to finance initial payments. That first payment on wheat delivered to the Pools was set at seventy cents. It seemed a safe bet that prices had hit bottom and would move upward. But prices went lower instead of higher and the seventy cents announced as initial payment was too high; it was dropped, and dropped again to fifty cents. Making the world situation worse, large amounts of Russian wheat were appearing, and by the middle of November, 1930, the trading price of wheat was fifty cents a bushel. It was plainly ruinous, but nobody knew how to reverse the trend.

What was to be done for Pool members? Some farmers renewed their call for 100 per cent compulsory Pools. Some Pool members were deserting. Pool debts were becoming higher. "Everything is tottering," A. J. McPhail wrote on November 30, 1930. Something had to be done, quickly.

Following a meeting of Pool officials, banks and provincial premiers, John I. McFarland, formerly of Alberta Pacific Grain Company, was named to take over the general management of the Pools. McFarland was probably the only man who could have accepted the gigantic responsibility with the confidence of all parties concerned. As it was, he had full authority to proceed as he thought best. He acted boldly, as he was expected to do, instituting a new selling policy. The London office was closed and Pool wheat was being sold on the Winnipeg Grain Exchange, embarrassing as it was bound to be to men who had worked for marketing reforms. For men like Wood and McPhail and Burnell, it was humiliating, heartbreaking. But they stood resolute, convinced the pooling principle was right and the Pools would survive. Amazingly, many farmers retained their faith in the Pools.

From a meeting in the summer of 1931, came a new Pool policy. In the face of ruinous prices, failure of the pooling programs in 1929 and 1930, and the prospect of an initial price no better than thirty-five cents on the 1931 crop, new marketing rules had to be drafted. All members were now to be released from the delivery terms of their contracts. In other words, they would be free to sell wheat how and where they chose. Those who cared to take the chance could continue pooling on a voluntary basis. But all members were urged to continue to use Pool elevators.

Actually, the change made at that time set policy for years ahead and the three Provincial Pools became instruments for handling grain more than for marketing. The Pools, with revised purpose, regained a place of commanding importance, and when a Canadian Wheat Board was set up with apparent permanency, the farmer-owned elevators were seen as proper supplements.

A. J. McPhail died when his beloved Wheat Pool was at the peak of dilemma, still carrying crushing debt. Henry Wise Wood continued as president of the Alberta Wheat Pool until 1937 when all three Pools were quite different in character from the humbled institutions of 1929.

What about the Pools' debts? Were they ever paid? Depression lingered for some years but the Pools persisted, mainly as elevator co-operatives. With the Wheat Board assuming the responsibility for sales, the Pools could specialize in elevators and farm services. It was revenue from the successful elevator programs which paid off the debts. Part of the Manitoba Pool debt was assumed by the Government of that province but in both Saskatchewan and Alberta, the Pools paid their debts in full.

PART IV

⟨⟩

DROUGHT YEARS AND RECOVERY

※ ♋ ↷

CHAPTER XXIV

THE HUNGRY THIRTIES

↷ ♋ ↷

There had been prolonged spells of drought and there had been economic depressions; but never before had Westerners witnessed anything to match the devastating combination of drought and depression which struck them in the thirties. Indians said it was a visitation by the Great Spirit, angry with the piratical ways of white men. It looked, indeed, as though both natural and economic laws had broken down. Considering hardships and losses, it was by far the worst blow felt by residents of the wheat country.

Western Canadians could expect dry years now and then, even two or three such years in a row. John Palliser sounded the first warning. But prairie people were optimists. When drought visited them in 1929, the popular observation was: "Oh, it's just one of those years we can expect occasionally; next year will be better." They recalled how 1921 had been dry and the next two years saw good crops. But the optimists were wrong this time, and the drought lingered as if to outclass and outlast the depression.

The price decline, beginning with the Market Crash of October, 1929, continued for several years, leaving producers shocked and discouraged. Market prices fell far below costs of production, and many people on the land faced ruin. For agricultural products, there was no exception; all met with the same buyer resistance. The average price for yearling steers at the Saskatchewan Feeder Show, Moose Jaw, in 1933, was $2.75 per hundred pounds. In 1934, the price was even lower; it was $2.35 and improvement came slowly. Market pigs sold for as low as $1.85 per hundred pounds. Eggs were known to sell at 3 cents per dozen and wheat on December 16, 1932, went to 39⅜ cents per bushel for Number One Northern at Fort William. It was the lowest price recorded for commercial wheat over a period of 300 years.

When freight and handling charges were deducted, it meant that the

net return to a grower was often less than 20 cents a bushel. On the day
Number One Northern wheat brought 39⅜ cents per bushel at Fort
William, Number Two Northern at Edmonton would have been worth
17½ cents per bushel and at Dawson Creek, on the British Columbia side
of the Peace River area, it would have brought 10½ cents. Barley of
3 C.W. grade, on the same day, would be priced at 8 cents per bushel at
Edmonton and 2 cents at Dawson Creek.

At such prices, growers could not make mortgage payments, and could
scarcely buy groceries. Some farmers accepted the great misfortune with
smiles, some with anger. Innisfail citizens saw an enraged farmer dump
a wagon load of barley on the main street. He had paid eight cents per
bushel to have the grain threshed and when the elevator agent offered
him seven cents, he drove out onto the street and pulled the end gate.

A Cayley farmer recalled his need for chewing tobacco and how
he gathered twelve dozen eggs to be used for trade at the store. The
big plug he wanted was priced at fifty-two cents. The storekeeper would
allow him four cents per dozen for the eggs. He was short four cents but
was able to borrow that much, and he went home with the essential plug of
chewing tobacco.

A story told many times concerned the farmer who took a wagon-
load of barley to the elevator, to be informed by the agent that deductions
for handling, dockage and excessive moisture, totaled more than the
barley was worth, and a net deficit of one dollar was payable to the
elevator. The bewildered farmer admitted that he did not have a dollar,
but would bring the agent a few dozen eggs or a dressed chicken. That
would be satisfactory, the agent replied. "Bring me a dressed chicken
and we'll be square." And the farmer, either not very bright or seizing
the chance to enhance the agricultural story, appeared in the elevator a
few days later with two dressed chickens. "But," said the elevator man,
"I told you I would settle for one chicken. What's the idea in bringing
me two?"

"I remember," the farmer replied, "you said I owed you one chicken,
but, today, I brought in another load of barley."

The notorious prices for wheat and barley and cattle were no more
ruinous than drought and drifting soil in those years. The drought started
in 1929, and except for a moderately good crop in 1932, failure was
rather general until 1938.

Drought was the chief cause for crop loss but it was not alone; the
crop of 1933 started with some indication of producing a harvest, but
grasshoppers brought ruin. And in 1935, the prairie crop gave some

reasons for optimism until rust and early autumn frosts brought widespread failure. Rust in Manitoba and Saskatchewan in that year caused crop damage in excess of $100,000,000.

All the while, every high wind scooped up enough dry soil to make a blinding dust storm. Nothing was more depressing than the almost constant presence of soil in the air. It was impossible to get away from the gritty dust. When the wind was high, soil in the air dulled the rays of the sun and made midday look like twilight. People inhaled dust when they breathed and chewed on the gritty stuff when they ate their meals. It entered houses through doorways and cracks around windows and settled as an ugly film on clothing, on furniture, on beds and dishes.

Worst of all, the best of the soil on many previously-productive fields was being blown away. Some fields lost just about everything, except stones, to the depth of a plow furrow.

It was difficult to see anything funny about the situation, but one of the farmers who did not lose all sense of humor told how the dust over his fields was extremely thick, and he saw a gopher digging a hole ten feet above the ground. Another, with poetic inclinations, sat down at night and wrote words for a song, entitled "Oh Where Is My Wandering Soil Tonight?"

At Swift Current there was a report about a man who fainted in church and there being no water available, his friends revived him by dashing a pail of dust in his face. And a farmer at Medicine Hat, when asked how much crop he expected to recover, said that if his binder would cut two inches below the ground surface, he would get his seed back.

For Saskatchewan and southern Alberta, the climax came in 1937 when Nature displayed her ugliest mood. Over the entire Midwest, wheat yields averaged 11.5 bushels in 1929, and in the next seven years exceeded that figure only once. Then, in 1937, yield dropped to 6.4 bushels, while Saskatchewan, with 14,000,000 acres planted to wheat, harvested only 36,000,000 bushels, about $2\frac{1}{2}$ bushels per acre. The Saskatchewan average for barley was 4.7 bushels and for oats, 5.1 bushels. Most threshing machines did not turn a wheel in that season.

On many prairie farms, the only crop harvested was Russian thistles, and trying to winter cattle and sheep on such extremely rough feed called for patience and ingenuity.

It was easy to conclude, as some editors and private observers did, that an important shift had occurred in climate, and wheat would never again be a safe and profitable crop. The time had come, they reasoned, to abandon the prairie farm lands for cultivation. Better to use them exclusively for grazing, they said. One editor, quite seriously, suggested restocking parts of the Prairies with buffaloes.

Land became unsalable. Construction came to a halt. One-third of automobile owners failed to buy licenses. Unemployment mounted. Sloughs went dry. Cash was the scarcest thing of all and a dollar bill "looked as big as a horse blanket." School Boards had their share of troubles. The Saskatchewan Government found it necessary to cut school grants by one-third, and boards cut salaries. The average annual salary for first class male teachers in rural schools in Saskatchewan in 1936 was $512 and for female teachers, $407.

Poverty was in evidence on every hand and governments were obliged to furnish relief on an unprecedented scale. Much of the cost of that relief was furnished by the Federal Government, but the provinces and municipalities were contributors also and were responsible for administration. For the fiscal year, 1937-38, Federal assistance to relief in Saskatchewan and Alberta was $30,000,000.

In addition to direct government relief, there were non-government contributors in large numbers. It would be difficult to determine the total value of gifts. The Government of Saskatchewan bought 550 carloads of potatoes for free distribution where they were needed. For special distribution in areas which suffered most over the eight preceding years, there were 285 carloads of apples, 142 carloads of turnips, 242 carloads of other vegetables, 220 carloads of fish and cheese and beans. Not all the food contributions were fit to eat. Some of the hard slabs of salted cod from the east coast defied the best Saskatchewan cooks and were used for repairing cracks in walls. But all the gifts were sent with the best of intentions and deserved appreciation.

In addition, there were the generous contributions classified as Voluntary Rural Relief: 309 carloads of mixed food from Ontario points; 133 carloads from British Columbia; 177 from Manitoba, parts of which province obtained a fair crop during the year; 35 carloads from Prince Edward Island; 28 from the Province of Quebec; altogether, 771 carloads from various parts of Canada in the single year of 1937-38.

The Red Cross accepted a special role in distributing clothing to children who could not have continued at school without such outside aid.

An important part of the emergency, falling to governments, was in finding feed for livestock. First of all, cattle and other farm animals which could be spared were shipped out of the area. About half a million cattle were removed from farms in Saskatchewan and Alberta during the year, thin ones to abattoirs for canning, some to feedlots in distant parts of the continent, and others to a big government pasture at Carberry, Manitoba. Then, to help feed the livestock remaining, feeds brought to the drought area under government auspices included 5,900,000 bushels of oats, 1,600,000 bushels of barley, 1,200,000 bushels of wheat, some corn and mill feeds, and 378,000 tons of hay.

That was the wheat country of 1937, drained of the buoyancy and optimism of earlier and better times. When the purchasing power of good crops of wheat was lost, nothing remained for the support of local economy. Thousands of people left the farms, some to reside in eastern Canada, some to go back to the Old Country, and some to look for work in prairie towns and cities.

Words printed on the side of a farm wagon being hauled eastward to an undetermined destination by a team of emaciated horses told a story of struggle:

"1929 — Dried out
1930 — Frozen out
1931 — Dried out
1932 — Hailed out
1933 — Grasshoppered out
1934 — Dried out
1935 — Rusted out
1936 — Dried out
1937 — Blown out
1938 — Moving out"

It would have been easy to conclude that the wheat country was "down and out," never to regain its former productivity. But western soil, capricious at the best of times, held more surprises and the best was yet to be realized.

CHAPTER XXV

OUT OF DUST STORMS AND DESPAIR

A long-range scheme for conservation and rehabilitation in the prairie section—home of the world's best wheat—was one of the few good things to come out of those bleak years of drought and drifting soil. With conditions as they appeared after six years of famine and near-famine, it was obvious that the area bounded, approximately, by the lines of John Palliser's Triangle, should be abandoned or rescued with the help of a sound rehabilitation program. There was some support for abandonment, but, fortunately, there were those people who believed the prairie wheat country could still become a great and saving asset to Canada and a world calling for bread.

Cactus and Russian thistle plants—lovers of dry soil—were the only forms of vegetation showing vigor when in the spring of 1935 the Parliament of Canada passed the Prairie Farm Rehabilitation Act and provided an appropriation with which to launch the first stages of an ambitious program. Nobody expected a miracle or even a rapid transformation of the run-down and blown-out land. Rehabilitation would take years, but the new plan—P.F.R.A.—it was hoped, would partially alleviate the distress and hasten the time when the area would once again be self-supporting.

The Hon. Robert Weir, Minister of Agriculture at the time, speaking in the House of Commons on April 10, 1935, said: "Throughout the whole program, it is our purpose to assist the farmers and demonstrate whether or not the people of these areas can continue to live there with only very little more moisture than they are now receiving. Our first aim is to do everything possible to make these people self-sustaining."

Understandably, the passing of an Act could not bring immediate relief. In fact, both the dust and drought problems became more irksome in 1937, the driest of all recorded years on the plains. The experiences of that year demonstrated better than anything preceding them that submarginal lands should be removed from cultivation, and something done to improve security on the remaining lands. Accordingly, the Act was amended to broaden its scope, making specific provision for the withdrawal of submarginal lands and resettlement of their occupants elsewhere. As for those lands to be withdrawn from cultivation and cereal production, what better could be done than to set them apart for regrassing and use as Community Pastures? Thereafter, P.F.R.A. objectives included searches for better cultural methods, safeguards against erosion, water development, irrigation, improved land use, and community pastures.

One of the first directors of the program was Scottish-born George Spence who homesteaded at Orkney in southwestern Saskatchewan, where frogs sometimes missed the opportunity to learn to swim. Spence had a passion for conserving water. To allow it to leave the more arid areas and flow to the oceans where it was not needed was only a little short of being a "crime," he contended. In the years following, the impounding of water received a big share of P.F.R.A. attention.

Water stored in reservoirs and behind dams found a multiplicity of uses in stock watering, irrigation, recreation, and meeting domestic needs. Whatever the uses, the Midwest gained thousands of bodies of water—large and small—which did not exist in earlier years. And all represented some measure of protection against the hazards associated with dry years.

Farmers wishing to improve their water resources could obtain the assistance of P.F.R.A. engineers in locating storage sites and doing the survey work. Finally, persons carrying out the construction work to the satisfaction of the federal officers could qualify for cash subsidies calculated on the basis of number of cubic yards of excavation. Water development undertakings, completed or assisted during the first thirty years after P.F.R.A. was launched, totaled over 90,000.

Those water conservation projects were of many kinds, ranging from the numerous small dugouts and dams constructed to meet farm needs, to huge irrigation schemes like the big St. Mary-Milk River Project which ultimately furnished water for almost half a million acres. The biggest undertaking of all was the South Saskatchewan River project at the Elbow, south of Saskatoon, designed for both hydro power and irrigation. Its gigantic rolled-earth dam rises to an impressive 210 feet in height. It was named to honor the Hon. James G. Gardiner[42] and was officially opened on July 21, 1967, climaxing nine years of building, and 109 years of discussion from the time the prairie explorer, Henry Youle Hind,[43] first saw the Saskatchewan River at that point and caught a vision of a dam.

No less successful than the water development program was the Community Pasture part of P.F.R.A. work. The fact was that the West had land which could be used more appropriately and profitably in growing pasture grass than in producing wheat. It was a matter of assessing land productiveness and turning the various parcels to their best use. Moreover, the idea of running privately owned cattle together on big, publicly owned pastures or ranges was sound, and farmers had talked about it almost half a century before the Federal Act was passed.

After the enabling amendment to the Act was passed in 1937, it was up to the Provincial Governments, desiring to take advantage of the plan for federal aid, to select areas in need of pasture development and formally request the Federal Government to fence, finance, and run the pastures. Farmers living on the land to be taken over for grazing had to be settled elsewhere. Watering facilities had to be provided or improved. Bare fields exposed to the dangers of soil erosion had to be protected, and fences, corrals, and equipment had to be provided.

Saskatchewan and Manitoba acted promptly to participate. In the very first year, sixteen Community Pastures, embracing a total of 177,-000 acres of marginal or submarginal land, were enclosed and made available to stockmen in the respective areas.

The program appeared as a special service to cattlemen, but it was more than that. It was a well-considered plan to achieve better land use, and wheat growers and all agricultural people had reason to be interested.

Among other things, the pastures were to offer demonstrations in rehabilitation of run-down land. In this, those responsible for policy were most successful. Because of dry years, erosion, and overgrazing, much of the land enclosed by the new pasture fences was extremely low in its productive capacity, so low, indeed, that it took an estimated fifty-eight acres on the average to support one unit of livestock or one cow. Eighteen years later, it could be reported that the carrying capacity of the pastures had been "more than trebled." How was this achieved? Native grasses were given opportunity to seed and rejuvenate themselves. Where this was not possible, areas were seeded with domestic grass, mainly the hardy and drought-resistant crested wheat grass. Roughly 200,000 acres were reseeded to domestic grass in the first few years.

Areas taken over for Community Pastures under P.F.R.A. grew to 2,000,000 acres serving 6,500 farmers who depended upon the pastures for grazing for their 140,000 cattle.

That was part of the story of achievement. There was resettlement of farmers on better lands, research in many aspects of conservation, demonstrations of improved agricultural practices, and so on. Prairie Farm Rehabilitation Act appeared as a good investment with grain growers and all citizens obtaining benefit.

P.F.R.A. policies and the expansion of irrigation were undoubtedly factors in prairie rejuvenation following the ills of the thirties, but the most potent reasons for recovery were to be found in the changed mood of weather and markets.

Better rains came with the war clouds in 1939, and the Midwestern provinces harvested 494,000,000 bushels, more than three times as much as in the crop season of two years before. The next year, 1940, was still better, with 513,000,000 bushels. It was only the second time—the first was in 1928 — that the West had produced above 500,000,000 bushels. It was reassuring, and more than an accident, because the area again produced over 500,000,000 bushels in 1942.

Although yields were encouraging, wartime demand for wheat was poor and prices remained low until the end of hostilities. Unsold wheat piled up in elevators and farm bins until World War II ended. Then Canada's wheat was wanted eagerly in Europe and elsewhere. The prairie wheat crop of 1937 had a value of $161,000,000; the corresponding figure for 1949, just twelve years later, was $529,000,000. It was hard to believe but the biggest yields of all were ahead — 529,000,000 bushels in 1951, and 664,000,000 bushels in 1952. Big yields in the fifties resulted in big carry-over volumes with quota deliveries and some discouragement. But Canada's wheat industry had still not reached its zenith; bigger yields, bigger markets, and bigger years were still to come.

CHAPTER XXVI

⚮

THE CANADIAN WHEAT BOARD

⚮

When Wheat Pools, in the early thirties, were fighting for survival, and the pooling system was collapsing, farmers were back — whether they liked it or not — to the sale of wheat through the facilities of the Winnipeg Grain Exchange. Prices were moving lower and lower and farmers called upon the Federal Government for a marketing board. They remembered 1919, remembered how the Canadian Wheat Board handled the crop of that year, and later made a participation payment very much resembling a bonus. There was magic in the Board name, and growers called for another Wheat Board, the only institution which, they believed, was capable of affording price protection.

People in government, on the other hand, wanted no more major roles in wheat marketing if it were possible to escape them. But something had to be done to rescue a crumbling western industry beset by crop failures as well as ruinously low prices. The average price of wheat at Saskatchewan points in 1932 was only thirty-five cents per bushel; in the next year it was forty-seven cents. In 1934 and 1935, it was sixty-one cents. With mounting insistence from wheat country farmers, the government members acknowledged a responsibility, and the Canadian Wheat Board Act was passed and given assent on July 5, 1935.

The Board, as appointed under the Act, was given authority to buy, store, transfer, and sell wheat—also to transfer a year's operating deficit to the Government of Canada. It had enough power to become a great force in both domestic and international trading circles. It could determine prices, but initial payments would be set annually by order in council.

The terminal date for each annual pool was July 31. When surplus money existed at the conclusion of the crop year, the Board was required to make distribution to producers on the basis of wheat delivered.

Settlement could take the form of a single final payment after the year's business was completed, or it might be made in two payments, an interim payment and then the final payment.

The principle of a late payment had its advantages as farmers noted in 1951, when owing to wet weather at harvest time, very little grain was threshed and marketed until the following spring. But with a final payment on the 1950 crop, farmers had some money.

In the first years, the Canadian Wheat Board operated on a voluntary and stand-by basis. Farmers had the choice of selling through the Board or on the open market. When the Board's initial payment, as in the first year, was bigger than the price to be realized on the open market, the Board could expect to get all or nearly all the wheat delivered. In that first year, 1935-36, the initial payment was 87½ cents per bushel, basis Number One Northern at Lakehead ports or Vancouver. This was higher than the open market price and the Board handled most of the year's crop, actually 150,700,000 bushels. With the initial payment already more than the Board could hope to recover in sales, the year's operations showed a loss of $12,000,000.

Growers realized, or should have realized, that under the Canadian Wheat Board plan the initial payment was like a floor price and Board losses, when they occurred, were simply charged to the public treasury. The Act had, for all practical purposes, placed the credit of the country behind the marketing of western wheat. Men on the land were reassured, even though the participation certificates distributed on the 1935 crop were valueless.

In each of the next two years, the initial price was unchanged at 87½ cents per bushel but effective only if the open market price at Fort William fell below 90 cents. As it turned out, the closing market price at the Lakehead did not fall below 90 cents for Number One Northern, and the Board did not accept wheat in either year. But when the crop of 1938 was coming to market, the Board was again taking deliveries, making an initial payment of 80 cents per bushel. On the year's operations, the Board's loss was $61,000,000.

Not until 1940-41, when the initial payment was 70 cents, did the Board have some surplus money for distribution, and when final settlement was made, the return to growers totaled a fraction over 76 cents at Fort William.

Following the outbreak of World War II, many of Canada's customary markets were cut off and the volume of unsalable wheat became big. There was a 500,000,000 bushel crop of wheat in the West and elevators were unable to accommodate the grain that farmers wanted to deliver. To give all growers an equal chance, delivery controls were necessary. Accordingly, the Wheat Board Act was amended to allow the Board to administer a quota system. For the first year, the quota was fixed at five bushels per authorized acre, then raised successively to eight bushels, ten bushels, twelve bushels, fifteen bushels, twenty bushels and finally, on April 21, 1941, farmers were told they could deliver on an "open quota" for the remaining part of the crop year.

Quotas were sources of annoyance to farmers as they were to those people who had to administer them, but they were regulations which nobody could condemn, and farmers accepted and became accustomed to them.

The Canadian Wheat Board's primary function was to sell grain and this it appeared to do well, reaching into far parts of the world. Those people who hoped this monster threatening to destroy the freedom of open markets would have a short life, were due for disappointment. In 1943, the Board was made the sole marketing agency for wheat, and as of August 1, 1949, oats and barley were added to its selling responsibilities.

Board duties and Board stature were growing. Having helped to establish confidence in the late thirties, the Wheat Board met the new circumstances created by World War II, adjusted to the postwar years of wheat scarcity, dealt judiciously with more years of surplus in the fifties, handled crops and sales of record proportions in the sixties, and held the confidence of grain growers across the West.

The Board did not escape criticism, but it was never seriously challenged. When the Canadian carry-over of wheat reached the disquieting level of 733,000,000 bushels at August 1, 1957, some cries were raised by individuals who thought private enterprise could have sold more wheat. Most wheat growers, however, were never convinced that the open market could have done better. They recalled the theory of Lord Keynes,[44] eminent British economist, who noted how the free market "abhors a surplus" and generally reacts with markedly lower prices. That was what wheat farmers hoped to avoid. Perhaps a surplus was the lesser of two dangers.

As the Wheat Board Act was drafted, it was subject to renewal by parliament every five years. There was never any parliamentary hesitation about extending its life, and many people wondered why it was necessary to repeat the renewal formality. Finally, in 1967, the Federal Government decided to bring down legislation making the Wheat Board a permanent institution. The fact that the proposal was approved without opposition in the House of Commons was seen as an indication of the high regard in which the role of the Board was held by wheat growers and most Canadians.

There was more criticism when jurisdiction over the Board was transferred from one department of government to another. Originally, the Canadian Wheat Board reported to parliament through the Minister of Trade and Commerce, but in 1960 a change was made and the Board was placed with the Department of Agriculture. Some farm organizations approved, but many observers doubted if the move was in the best interests of Canadian producers and Canadian trade. Anyway, there came another change of government in 1963, and the Wheat Board was rather promptly returned to Trade and Commerce.

The Board did not and could not meet all producer demands, but it did one thing to general grower satisfaction: inasmuch as the initial payment announced at the beginning of each crop year was, in essence, a floor price, farmers from 1935 forward could enjoy a feeling of protection against a disastrous slump in trade. Moreover, they had appreciation for a marketing plan by which returns were equitable for all. Payments could vary only because of differences in freight costs and grades.

Never have growers wished to gamble on a fluctuating market with their year's crop of grain. It happened too often in the years of open markets that farmers sold their product at the "wrong" time and lost heavily. They prefer a uniform price throughout the year and the Wheat Board form of guarantee against a serious price collapse. They like the idea of a Wheat Board and will fight to retain it.

CHAPTER XXVII

⊱⊙⊰

THE WAR AGAINST RUST

⊰⊙⊱

While drought and depression continued to hold a savage grip upon the wheat country, the first of a spectacular succession of new varieties made their appearance. These were triumphs for the plant breeder, for they demonstrated the breeders' important role in helping growers to overcome certain production problems, stem rust and wheat stem sawfly for example, just as Charles Saunders had helped in combating losses from early frosts.

Unlike Saunders, the new generation of plant breeders was equipped with a knowledge of genetics, without which they could not have made the great strides of success against the plant enemies, particularly stem rust. The finest demonstration of all was in the creation of rust-resistant varieties like Thatcher, Apex, and Renown which appeared in the thirties.

Stem rust was a sneaky and treacherous enemy, capable of bounding from what seemed like nowhere to deal destruction upon crops approaching maturity. That was the way it appeared in 1916 when a good harvest of Marquis wheat seemed certain. Farmers who knew what it was to be dried out, hailed out, and frozen out were quite unfamiliar with this invisible destroyer which caused healthy wheat plants to become suddenly sick and deteriorate to failure in late July and early August. Farmers felt utterly helpless.

Crop losses in 1916 were placed at $200,000,000, and growers were fearful that the disease would return in the next and succeeding years. Some cast about for simple controls like treating seed or planting at a "right" time of the moon. Some weird remedies were suggested, but those people who listened to the scientists knew that the life history of the rust fungus, the microscopic organism causing the trouble, was a most involved affair and a farmer had no chance of stopping the disease if weather conditions were favorable for it and if the infection was present. They were told that the full life cycle was not completed in the Canadian West.

The fact was that spores, responsible for a new infection during the Canadian crop year, had to come from far south where the fungus was able to winter over — perhaps on winter wheat — and be ready to multiply in the spring. Anyway, the tiny spores had to come floating in on southerly air currents, explaining why rust was always noticed first in southern Manitoba and southeastern Saskatchewan in epidemic years.

An understanding of the life cycle was to change many of the old theories about control. The early view was that rust infection lived over from one year to the next to perpetuate itself where it had struck. In 1904, a year of rust attack in Manitoba, farm magazines advised farmers to burn stubble and butts from old straw piles in order to destroy the rust organisms which might otherwise survive to plant the infection in the succeeding crop. But such advice was pointless when it became apparent that each new infection had to be introduced on breezes from the south.

The essential point was that incoming spores could settle on prairie crops, and if weather conditions were favorable — damp and muggy — the fungus would multiply. New generations of red spores would appear in rapid-fire order and these could extend the infection to other areas of crop. Damage was being done as the organisms multiplied; crop plants were sapped and weakened. Heads of grain failed to fill, and farmers, at this point, knew there was little or nothing they could do about it. If the rust attacked early, it could mean total loss of the crop; if it attacked late, it might mean partial loss.

Late in the season, the rust fungus would produce black spores on straw and leaves. These black ones could not infect grain or grass directly but could winter over and if they found a host plant of their liking, they could complete their cycle. The host plant they required was not grain at all; rather, it was the common barberry.

Obviously, farmers could not afford to have barberry bushes. Because efforts to keep them out of western provinces were successful, the fungus was unable to complete its life cycle in those parts. It was bad enough to have spores blowing in from a distance; it would be worse if the source of new infections existed right in the area. Moreover, it was only at the sexual stage on barberry that new rust strains were formed.

Common barberry, not a native of North America, was one of those plants introduced to the continent by early settlers from Europe.

Actually, rust was not a new plant disease, not by any means. The microscopic rust spores were floating about Mediterranean countries 2,000 years ago. In western Canada, it was only in 1916 that the disease received full attention. The losses of that year were serious, but they led to an organized attack upon the enemy and to ultimate successes which brought huge benefits to Canadian grain growers.

What the plant breeders achieved, represented one of the greatest practical triumphs in the history of science. Dr. W. P. Thompson of the University of Saskatchewan observed that while common bread wheat surrendered readily to rust, certain emmer wheats and other kinds were highly resistant. At a conference held in Winnipeg, Dr. Thompson— later President of the University of Saskatchewan—proposed a breeding program aimed at finding or making a rust-resistant variety retaining the good features of Marquis.

The creation of Marquis was the plant breeders' first major success in bringing benefit to the West. Its introduction continued to stand as the greatest single event in the story of western Canadian progress. But after Marquis there was nothing very spectacular in new wheat varieties for some years, and the proposal of 1916, to create a new wheat especially to meet a need, must have sounded fantastic to those who observed critically: "You can't hope to take wheat varieties apart, reshuffle the pieces and put them together to suit you."

The plant breeders replied: "Perhaps we can regroup the genes and come up with the combinations we want."

The work progressed slowly at first but in 1924, with the National Research Council, the Federal Department of Agriculture and western universities co-operating, an Associate Committee on Cereal Rust was set up and an action program drafted. Plans were drawn for a federal laboratory which was established as the Dominion Rust Research Laboratory on the campus of the University of Manitoba on Winnipeg's south side. It was opened in 1925.

Similar work was planned and undertaken in the United States. In 1931, Minnesota announced the first major success, a new variety of spring wheat with approved milling qualities, good yield, and resistance to the crop enemy, stem rust. Moreover, it was said to be earlier than Marquis and to have a slightly heavier yield. They called it Thatcher. In 1936, a quantity of this new wheat with Marquis as a double grandparent was brought to western Canada and became very popular.

In the meantime, 1935 to be exact, two new wheat varieties were announced by Canadian workers, Renown, from the Dominion Rust Research Laboratory, and Apex, from the Field Husbandry Department of the University of Saskatchewan. Four years later, the Dominion Rust

Research Laboratory announced another rust-resistant variety, this one called Regent. And in 1946, still another one came from the same laboratory, Redman. It is not to be overlooked that all of these new varieties of rust-resistant wheats had Marquis somewhere in their pedigrees, accounting, no doubt, for the high milling qualities being perpetuated.

To the casual observer, the old rust demon seemed to be beaten. But such conclusions were premature. The stem rust enemy had been repulsed but not defeated. While the plant breeders were making new varieties, Nature in her subtle way was fashioning new strains of the rust and a virulent form known as race 15B was detected. It was a strain against which Thatcher and Redman and the other so-called rust-resistant wheats could not stand. With all possible haste plant breeders went to work to find an entirely new wheat and as luck would have it, a new source of breeding material in the form of a rust-resistant wheat was found growing in a Manitoba farm field. The new discovery was named McMurchy and from crosses between it and other selected lines, the Canada Department of Agriculture workers at Winnipeg produced Selkirk wheat with resistance against all the prevalent races of stem rust, including 15B.

Distribution of Selkirk began in 1953, but in the very next year, while seed stock was still in short supply, rust of the 15B kind struck the western grain fields. The older varieties which had served well for a time went down before the new attack, and the farm losses seemed to be close to $150,000,000. The demand for Selkirk seed became keen, and for some years Selkirk was the dominant variety in Manitoba and southeastern Saskatchewan.

The scientists dared not rest. They knew that other forms of rust would appear, some of them extremely dangerous. In 1959, the Winnipeg workers came out with Pembina, a variety having resistance to some additional forms of rust. At the same time, they were talking about still other strains against which neither Selkirk nor Pembina would offer protection. Again they had to press for a new variety with all the qualities Canadian agriculture demanded, high milling value, good yield, early maturity — and resistance to all the rusts constituting threats. It was another big assignment, but an answer came in a variety licensed in 1965, Manitou, another success for the rust research workers and plant breeders. This hard red spring wheat came from backcrosses with Thatcher and promised to equal Thatcher in yield while offering rust resistance far greater than Thatcher possessed. There was no guarantee, of course, that tricky new strains of rust would not appear to prey upon Manitou also.

In their battle against rust, plant breeders could hope to keep ahead of the enemy but not to vanquish it.

The possibilty of finding an effective chemical weapon for use against rust was never overlooked, and, with many advances in agricultural chemistry, the chances of an important discovery were increased. The use of field machinery in applying a fungicide, at a time when grain crops were far advanced, would do serious damage however, and this would have to be considered. In the meantime, farmers knew they had to rely upon varieties with "built-in" resistance, and hoped that plant breeders working at research institutions would be able to keep at least apace of the treacherous plant disorder.

A similar story could be told about the plant breeders' success in creating varieties to meet other situations. Rescue and then Chinook wheats were bred expressly to give protection against wheat stem sawfly, the small insect which lays eggs in wheat stems. The plant breeders came forward with varieties having solid stems through which the sawfly grubs were unable to burrow, and farmers in the affected areas planted with new confidence.

There have been many forcible reminders of the crop growers' dependence upon the men working in research institutions. Only with the help of scientific workers are Canadian growers able to remain in the forefront of world production.

CHAPTER XXVIII

CHANGING WAYS IN THE WHEAT FIELDS

Change has been the order of things in the western wheat fields. Size of farms, varieties of wheat, cultivation techniques, marketing policies, safeguards against crop failure, sources of field power, costs of production, and harvesting methods changed. Just about everything has changed except the high quality of western wheat. It is a moving story. A grower of 1907 would be a bewildered stranger on a representative farm of sixty years later.

The typical wheat grower of 1907 was a horse farmer. A few of his homesteading neighbors might still be using oxen but would be hoping for horses as soon as finances would permit. The manufacturers of steam tractors were trying to win public interest in heavy equipment, but there seemed to be only the slightest chance that horses would ever be displaced as the major means of field power.

The typical half-section wheat farmer had nine draught horses of Clydesdale or Percheron breeding and one driving horse for the road. He aimed to raise a foal or two each year for replacement purposes. Every farmer was a horseman, with skill in breaking colts, treating colic, repairing harness, and driving a four-horse or six-horse outfit with four reins. He left his bed early enough every morning to feed horses at five o'clock, clean stables at half past five and groom and harness at six. Every day was a long day, ending at some time after the evening meal, when a final trip was made to the stable to shake down the bedding, check the mangers for hay, and be assured that no horse was afflicted with colic.

Horses survived the attempts by salesmen of steam tractors to dislodge them in the wheat fields. They then withstood the challenge from big and cumbersome gasoline tractors. But there came smaller gasoline tractor models, faster, cheaper and more versatile, and farmers wanted them. Nothing changed wheat production methods so much as the mechanization of field operations.

In the dramatic power revolution, horse numbers fell and tractors increased in number. It happened across the nation but was most noticeable in the West. Canada, in 1921, had 3,610,494 horses and only 38,600 farm tractors. Most of the tractors and 2,294,403 of the horses—63 per cent—were on the 255,657 farms of Manitoba, Saskatchewan and Alberta where their work was mainly in the wheat fields. Ten years later Canada's horses had decreased by some 400,000 and tractors had increased to 105,-360. Conversion was the trend, and by 1961 the Canadian horse population was down to 512,021 and tractor numbers were up to 549,789, or 114 tractors per 100 farms. With horses averaging about one per farm it was obvious that tractors had taken over the heavy toil in agricultural fields. In the West, the 290,700 tractors represented 138 of the mechanical things for every 100 farms, and horsehairs on farmers' clothing had vanished completely.

As the trend was to bigger farm units, so demand swung to bigger tractors. A farm operator would buy a bigger power unit rather than hire an extra man. By 1967, the most popular selling lines were in tractors of 60 to 80 horsepower. Manufacturers were expecting the farm request to be for still bigger machines.

With tractors came new harvesting equipment like combines, which reduced the need for big harvesting crews and served to relegate binders to fence corners. Gone were the Harvester Excursions which had been the means of introducing thousands of Easterners to the wheat fields and the West, transporting them from any point in the East to Winnipeg for $15, and from Winnipeg to point of destination for half a cent a mile. Gone were the intestinal disorders induced by drinking alkali water, making many of the Easterners wish they had never left home. Gone were the stooking crews which tried valiantly to keep up with binders. Gone were the household problems in cooking for huge crews with unfathomable appetites.

In 1931, there were only 8,917 of the harvesting combines in Canada, with all but 20 of them being in Alberta, Saskatchewan and Manitoba. But by 1961, there were 155,611 in Canada, with 81 per cent of them in the three Midwestern provinces; 65 out of every 100 farms in the West had them.

The new machines made agriculture more efficient and greatly extended the productive capacity of the fewer farm workers. But modern machines were costly, adding much to the capital needed by anyone starting in the business. The census of 1966 placed the value of machines and equipment on Canadian farms at $3,552,411,400. A man starting on a farm of average size needed at least $20,000 for power and machinery—a very different need from that which faced his father or grandfather who had started with two horses and a walking plow.

The adoption of mechanization led not only to bigger farms but to fewer farms. For Canada as a whole, the average farm of 1921 had 198 acres. Forty years later, the figure was 359. And in the Midwest, where farms were always bigger than in the East, the average size in 1921 was 322 acres, and in 1961 it was 609 acres or just a little less than one section.

Between 1951 and 1961, Canadian farms decreased in number by 23 per cent, and increased in size by 28 per cent. Many people wondered where the trend would stop. Farm population in relation to total Canadian population fell steadily from 75 per cent at the time of Confederation to 31.7 per cent in 1931, then 27.4 per cent in 1941 and 11.4 per cent in 1961. Again, the trend was most pronounced in the wheat country.

But mechanization, although the most important, was only one of several factors responsible for revolutionary changes in wheat farming. There were the improved varieties, of course, the adoption of bookkeeping and business management, and the acceptance of fertilizers, insecticides and herbicides. One way or another, production per worker has increased many times.

Although the element of risk has not been removed from grain farming it has been reduced, partly through improved practices, partly by government policies. The government-instituted safeguards included Prairie Farm Assistance Act and then Crop Insurance.

Known most commonly as P.F.A.A., the Prairie Farm Assistance Act was applicable in the prairie country and the Peace River section of British Columbia. Passed by the Federal Parliament in 1939, it was intended as an aid in keeping people on their farms at a time when agriculture still felt the hardships of drought and depression. It embraced some of the features of both relief and crop insurance, but government spokesmen insisted that it was neither. Farmers were to contribute 1 per cent of grain sales, and the Government of Canada was to make up any difference needed to support payments made in areas of low crop yield. There was no program in 1942, but with that single omission, between 1939 and 1965, payments totalled $353,016,572. Farmers, up to that time, contributed about half of the money distributed.

There were criticisms of P.F.A.A. Payments were decided on the basis of average yields in a township or other big block, and the misfortune of individual farmers seemed to escape attention. The maximum payment of $800—based on $4 an acre in the lowest yield category and half the

seeded acreage up to 400 acres—would not go far in paying expenses on
a big farm. The large-scale operators paid more in deductions but received
no more in return. Finally, there was the danger that P.F.A.A. was keeping
people on submarginal farms when such land should have been taken out
of cultivation and marked for grazing.

There was no doubt about the Act's usefulness in providing a measure
of protection but something more was needed, and the Parliament of
Canada, in 1959, passed enabling legislation to allow provinces to institute
crop insurance. All-risk insurance had been the subject of debate and
studies for decades. A Royal Commission appointed by the Government of
Manitoba reported in 1955 that crop insurance was beyond the ordinary
economic resources of the province.

An effort of consequence was made in 1936 when United States'
President Roosevelt named a committee to study all-risk insurance, which
led, two years later, to legislation to provide for the Federal Crop
Insurance Corporation. The new body offered crop insurance on wheat in
1939 and on cotton in 1942. But payments exceeded premiums by so much
that the plan was discontinued in 1944, then reinstituted in a revised form.

There was wide agreement that crop insurance was hazardous, too
hazardous for private companies; and even governments were reluctant to
become involved. But, as finally set forth in the Canadian act, the Federal
Government was prepared to offer some financial inducements. There was
to be no compulsion in crop insurance, but the Government would pay
50 per cent of administrative costs and 20 per cent of premiums.

Manitoba was the first province to take it up and operated with 3,675
farmers covered in 1960. Saskatchewan entered in a modest way in 1961,
and the Legislature of Alberta, at the session of 1964, provided authoriza-
tion to participate.

What some people see in the numerous changes is an end to the
traditional family farms. The trend, they reason, is to big, corporation-type
farms, highly mechanized and operated like factories. It requires only a
little imagination to see farmers of the future sitting in comfortable living
rooms, directing all field operations by push buttons.

Farms are calling for specialization and more efficiency, true enough,
and operators require more and broader working knowledge. They need
a knowledge of chemistry for weed control; engineering for getting the
most from high-priced machinery; biology for dealing with plant and
animal breeding; soils for getting the most from plantings; meteorology
for understanding weather modification; accounting for coping with
income tax; economics for meeting marketing problems.

But size of farm is not an indication of efficiency. Some of the best demonstrations of efficiency in agriculture are to be seen on the small farms of Holland and Denmark. Those who look to the day when Canada's agriculture will be handled by "just a few hundred corporations" are not likely to see the dream come true. Surely, the country would be poorer if family units were to disappear, just as it would be unfortunate if small businesses, owned by people running them, were to disappear.

There is no rule to show how big a family farm should be. A quarter-section wheat farm may very well be too small to allow the best use of machinery and supervision, but a quarter section devoted mainly to pigs or poultry or potatoes can be a big operation.

Anyway, the prophecies about huge factory farms make better news than logic, and there is reason to believe the medium-sized, owner-operated farms will compete successfully with the mammoth industrialized operations. Back of the reasoning is sentiment as well as conviction; without the so-called family farms—big or small as they may be—many of the best features in Canadian agriculture would be lost and the voice of agriculture would be feeble.

The family-type farms in Canada's past were not always paragons of efficiency and they did not produce fortunes, but they furnished opportunity for independence, useful employment, and valuable training ground for boys and girls. They also provided big markets for consumer goods made in cities. The West—and all of Canada—seems still to need that kind of agricultural enterprise.

PART V

❧

BREAD FOR A NEEDY WORLD

CHAPTER XXIX

INTERNATIONAL PLANNING

Western wheat farmers, plagued by instability in the world markets, talked hopefully about the possibility of long-term commodity agreements between exporting and importing countries, something to minimize the price fluctuations which seemed to work so frequently to the grower's disadvantage. Wheat Pools and Wheat Boards served to remove many of the local irritations. After World War II, the time had come to do something to make export trade more orderly. The idea appealed to producers in the United States, as well as in Canada, and a conference was proposed. The governments of thirty-five importing countries, caught in a period of relatively short supplies and high prices, were sufficiently interested to send representatives to an International Wheat Conference in London in 1947.

Discussions lasted for six weeks and resulted in an acceptable basis for an agreement which would have provided a maximum price of $1.80 and a starting minimum of $1.40 per bushel. Representatives were encouraged by the apparent progress, until near the end of the meetings when the United Kingdom spokesman took strong exception to the price, which he considered excessive. The conference ended without gaining its full purpose.

A similar conference was held in Washington the next year, with delegates from thirty-six nations in attendance. There was evidence of headway in reaching an accord for the sale of 500,000,000 bushels of wheat per year for five years, with the maximum price to be set at $2.00 per bushel, and the minimum starting at $1.50 per bushel and dropping ten cents per bushel per year.

The three exporting countries—Canada, the United States and Australia—and thirty-three importing countries accepted the plan, but before becoming binding, it had to be ratified by governments of countries concerned. It happened to be a year of presidential election in the United

States, and the agreement was not ratified there and did not go into effect.

Even though unsuccessful in its conclusion, the pioneer effort was seen to be worth while, and those people who recognized merit in an International Agreement were anxious to try again. Early in 1949, representatives from fifty-seven countries returned to Washington. Present for the first time were delegates from Russia, asking for a share of the export market. Other exporters were glad to have Russia in the plan, but they could not agree to the big share of exports being demanded by that country. In the end, thirty-seven importing countries undertook to purchase from the five exporting countries—Canada, the United States, Australia, France and Uruguay—456,000,000 bushels of wheat per year, for four years, at not less than $1.50 per bushel in the first year, $1.40 per bushel in the second year, $1.30 per bushel in the third year, and $1.20 per bushel in the fourth year. At the same time the exporting nations agreed to sell the named quantities of wheat at prices not to exceed $1.80 per bushel. Canada's allotment was 203,069,635 bushels per year.

Most governments ratified the plan and the first International Wheat Agreement—actually a multilateral treaty—went into effect in 1949 with objectives as stated: "To assure supplies of wheat to importing countries and markets for wheat to exporting countries at equitable and stable prices."

The value of the resulting International Wheat Agreement was often the subject of debate. Advocates of free markets asked how Canadian farmers could hope to obtain maximum prices for their wheat, while agreeing through the trading pact to keep trade within a limited range of prices. But most wheat growers liked the added stability and protection against serious drops in prices. Through the years, when the Agreement was being renewed, Canadian representatives, with support from farm organizations, played leading parts.

After operating for eighteen years, however, the International Wheat Agreement felt the winds of change. The renewed agreement of 1962—the fifth International Wheat Agreement to be signed—established a price range extending from $1.62½ per bushel to $2.02½ per bushel, United States funds, basis Number One Northern at Fort William and ten exporting countries and twenty-six importing countries were party to it. It seemed to be serving its purpose with general satisfaction. When it came up for renegotiation three years later it was extended without amendment for one year, and then extended for still another.

But new conflicts of interest arose. Canada and other exporting countries were pressing for higher world prices while importing nations were resisting. Almost everything else coming to the market place was advancing in price. It was difficult for growers, faced with greater costs, to see why they should not have the benefit of larger returns. At the same time, importers were anxious to check rising costs of living.

It was decided that if no understanding could be reached before July 31, 1967, the administrative machinery of the International Wheat Council would be maintained, but the Agreement would be allowed to lapse. The Council would continue to assemble data and furnish information, but be powerless to direct or regulate trade. Exporting and importing countries would be relieved completely of all previous obligations with respect to wheat prices and deliveries. The change in events suggested the possibility of a return to dumping and price-cutting. Canadian producers who saw the Agreement as the most successful attempt ever made in gaining orderly distribution of food were worried.

Fortunately, negotiations on prices were not abandoned, but continued at Geneva under the Kennedy Round discussions. By the time the July 31, 1967, deadline was reached, the old International Wheat Agreement had lapsed but a new Cereal Agreement was concluded under the General Agreement on Trade and Tariffs, by which countries accepting it approved an increase of about twenty cents per bushel over the floor and ceiling figures named in the previous International Wheat Agreement. The new prices would be on the basis of Number Two Hard Winter Wheat in store at Gulf of Mexico ports instead of Number One Northern, Fort William. There was reason for the change. It had to be admitted that Number One Northern was a rather rarely-encountered grade and Fort William was an ice-bound port for some months every year. To determine the Canadian equivalent of a ceiling of $2.13 in United States funds for Number Two Winter Wheat beside the Gulf of Mexico, a person would have to adjust for grade, freight, and exchange rates on money. It would be confusing at first, but Canadian growers knew they could not always have settlements on their own terms.

But the new international pact made no attempt to define quantities of wheat to be traded, and moreover, it could not come into effect until August 1, 1968. In the meantime, prices dropped below the minimums set in the new agreement, bringing pressures upon the Government of Canada to furnish support and making Canadian growers more convinced than ever that an international agreement was needed. The idea of a more definitive pact, something to take the place of the former International Wheat Agreement but retaining the prices adopted by the General Agreement on Trade and Tariffs, was being pursued.

While awaiting a more favorable world agreement and seeing prices dropping, Canadian wheat producers renewed an old request for government subsidies. Growers, noting how producers of many other commodities collected subsidies in one form or another, argued that they, too, should enjoy needed help from the public treasury. On the other hand, members of government hesitated about buying wheat at a set price and selling it for less on the world market, charging the difference to the taxpayers of Canada.

The point is that the growers of Canada need an International Wheat Agreement.

CHAPTER XXX

❦

THE WORLD OF WHEAT

❦

Canadians could not escape an interest in the international aspects of wheat and other foods. That particular grain, more than anything the country had to sell, made Canada a familiar name in world circles. People who were unimpressed by pulpwood, oil, and iron ore were quick to translate wheat to flour and bread. In the same way, wheat induced Canadian farmers to become students of international affairs. Growers in at least half a dozen countries entered into direct competition for world markets, and consumers in many and remote parts became Canadian customers. For very practical reasons, prairie farmers were interested in both the competitors and the customers. They could not afford to be otherwise.

Growing conditions in the United States, Australia, Argentina, and Russia, as well as consumer appetites and moods in the United Kingdom, Germany, Japan, and a score of other countries, reflected upon Canadian wheat fortunes, and forced growers to gaze far beyond their own line fences. For the best of reasons, western farmers found themselves studying reports about weather in Australia, famine in India, political moods in France, and successes and reverses in the European Common Market.[45]

Canadian growers, with searching gazes upon other lands, were mainly concerned with wheat, but they could not ignore other cereals like rice, rye, corn, barley, oats, sorghum and millet. Although not grown in Canada, rice has to be seen as one of the world's leading food crops, one upon which Asia's millions depend mainly for food. As a high-yielding cereal and one responding to intensive cultivation and care, it is well suited to the needs of the over-crowded East. Ninety per cent of the world's rice production is in Asia.

In nutritional value, rice resembles wheat in its high carbohydrate content but is lower in protein than wheat. A grain containing more protein would bring great benefit in parts of the world where meat and milk are only rarely available. But in furnishing food volume and calories in those areas where famines occur with shocking frequency, rice continues to offer more than any other cereal is likely to do.

In volume and value of products moving in international channels, however, wheat was, for many years, the unchallenged leader. Rather consistently, from the opening of the West, Canada has ranked first or second among the suppliers. Both Russia and the United States possess more arable land and greater production potential, but only the United States has surpassed in overseas shipments.

For many years, Canada, with a relatively small consuming population, led all countries in annual exports. Ultimately, however, United States' production soared far beyond domestic needs and that country became the leading exporter—also the country with the biggest annual surplus of wheat and the biggest domestic problems arising from wheat policies.

World demand, reacting to a rapidly expanding population and a growing preference for wheat over certain other bread grains, was generally upward, and production responded, reaching a record of 10,000,000,000 bushels in 1966. The increase of 7 per cent over the previous record of 9,360,000,000 bushels in 1964, was due, mainly, to Russia's exceptionally big crop, said to have totaled 2,734,000 bushels. Of the world's total in that year, the western Canadian wheat fields accounted for 824,000,000 bushels or a little more than 8 per cent.

According to figures appearing in *Canada Year Book,* 1966, based on estimates made by the Foreign Agricultural Service of the United States Department of Agriculture, North America, in 1964, was first among the continents with wheat to share, but Asia was first in total wheat acreage and Europe was first in total production. Quite obviously, wheat was grown extensively on all continents except Antarctica. The 1964 figures showed:

Asia	149,650,000 acres, yielding	1,940,000,000 bushels
North America	80,910,000 acres, yielding	1,970,000,000 bushels
Europe	72,020,000 acres, yielding	2,220,000,000 bushels
South America	18,820,000 acres, yielding	430,000,000 bushels
Oceania	18,161,000 acres, yielding	388,000,000 bushels
Africa	17,830,000 acres, yielding	220,000,000 bushels

On the basis of these figures, the average wheat yield was 30 bushels per acre for Europe, 24 bushels per acre for North America, 23 bushels per acre for South America, 21 bushels per acre for Oceania, 13 bushels for Asia, and 12 bushels for Africa. For the entire world, the total of

9,170,000,000 bushels, coming from 517,990,000 acres, represented an average of 17½ bushels per acre.

Which were the leading countries in wheat production? Russia, with 160,600,000 acres in wheat, was said to have harvested 2,000,000,000 bushels, thus showing an average yield of 12½ bushels per acre. The United States, with 1,290,468,000 bushels from 49,170,000 acres, could report a yield of 26 bushels per acre. India, with 356,000,000 bushels from 32,878,000 acres, had 11 bushels per acre, and needed a lot more to feed the hungry millions. Turkey's 260,000,000 bushels from 19,770,000 acres represented an average of roughly 13 bushels to the acre. And Canada's 29,685,000 acres, returning 600,424,000 bushels, worked out to about 20 bushels per acre.

A record for volume of wheat entering export channels came with the crop year of 1965-66. Of the approximately 10,000,000,000 bushels of world production, 2,297,000,000 bushels went into international trade. This was double the amount going into exports a decade earlier.

Of the total amount exported in that year of record shipments, almost 2,000,000,000 bushels were supplied by the United States, Canada, Australia and Argentina, known as the Big Four wheat exporters.

For many years, the Big Four countries provided over half of the world's wheat exports. In 1965-66, the Big Four shipments actually totaled 1,927,000,000 bushels, with the United States accounting for 859,000,000 bushels; Canada, 583,000,000 bushels; Argentina, 283,000,000 bushels; and Australia, 193,000,000 bushels.

For some years prior to that year of heavy exports, all members of the Big Four held large surplus volumes of wheat. Even at July 31, 1966, marking the end of the crop year of 1965-66, the four countries had a carry-over totaling 1,630,000,000 bushels. Two-thirds of that surplus was in the United States.

Canada's exports for the year in question represented slightly more than 30 per cent of total Big Four sales to overseas markets. In most years, Canada's exports represented more than 25 per cent of the wheat total shipped by Big Four countries.

Over the fifteen-year period, 1951-52 to 1965-66, the Canadian volume of exports ranged from a low point of 252,000,000 bushels in 1955-56 to a high point of 594,000,000 bushels in 1963-64.

There are many advantages in having wheat for the export trade. The most obvious is in gaining foreign exchange; wheat has brought Canada as much as $1,000,000,000 of foreign credit in a year. Almost as obvious is the international recognition and prestige enjoyed by a country having wheat to sell. There can be no doubt; furnishing wheat for export makes the country well known to people in distant parts. Men who do not know and do not care about Canada's leading position in exporting nickel and zinc and asbestos and newsprint, become very conscious of the country's good fortune in having wheat lands capable of furnishing grains for use at home and sales abroad.

CHAPTER XXXI

⚮

OLD CUSTOMERS AND NEW

⚮

Of Canada's traditional customers for wheat, the United Kingdom was as unfailing as an Atlantic tide. Not only were the Britishers the most dependable but they were generally the biggest purchasers. Other countries might buy spasmodically, but British millers knew exactly what they wanted and varied their year-to-year purchases only slightly. Canadians came to expect the United Kingdom representatives to take 100,000,000 bushels per year.

Disputes arose but not often. One of the rare controversies followed the postwar British-Canadian Wheat Agreement. Did the British pay enough or did the Canadian growers receive enough for wheat delivered under that four-year pact?

British interests wanted to be sure of supplies, and Canadian growers wanted to be sure of a market with fair prices over a period of years. It was the sentiment of most farmers that Canada should attempt to buy a measure of market security, even at the risk of somewhat reduced prices. By the terms of the four-year agreement signed on August 7, 1946, Canada undertook to furnish, and the United Kingdom undertook to take 600,000,000 bushels of wheat at prices which, in the light of changing world trade, proved to be too low.

The alleged injustice was proclaimed loudly by certain editorial writers as well as by advocates of a free and open market. Farmers, who at first were happy enough with the added security of a four-year contract, began to see the agreement as a bad bargain. They became critical and annoyed.

For the first two years of the contract, Canada was to supply 160,000,000 bushels of wheat per year at $1.55 per bushel. For the third year, the commitment was for 140,000,000 bushels at $1.25 per bushel, and for the fourth year, 140,000,000 bushels at $1.00 per bushel. As the agreement was drawn, however, the actual prices for the third and fourth years were subject to renegotiation if world prices happened to be higher than contract prices. As matters developed, world prices were, indeed, higher than the Canadian prices which seemed to be "frozen" by the terms of agreement. As most observers noted, the deal favored the buyers more than the sellers. In guessing the future of the world trade in wheat, British negotiators proved to be superior to their Canadian counterparts.

Critics of controlled marketing lost no opportunity to remind farmers of the sacrifices they were being asked to make for the benefit of both United Kingdom and Canadian consumers. Sure enough, farmers growing and selling wheat at contract prices when world prices ruled higher were subsidizing consumers on both sides of the Atlantic. The complaints did not go unnoticed, but both British and Canadian Governments assumed defensive positions.

In September, 1947, the British Government agreed to pay $2 per bushel for wheat from the 1948 crop. The revised price was still below world values, and many responsible Canadians believed the United Kingdom had not discharged its obligation, that another payment should be made. In 1951, the British Government was approached and asked to make a compensating payment to the western farmers who had been making it possible for the overseas consumers to eat cheap bread. But the Old Country spokesmen, although admitting the terms of sale had turned out to be a losing proposition for Canadian growers, pointed to their own record in living up to the terms of an agreement. They would do no more.

Finally, the Government of Canada appropriated $65,000,000 to be paid to western farmers, thereby admitting that the agreement, drawn with the best of intentions, left growers to bear the cost of supplying cheap wheat and flour for both Canadian and United Kingdom consumers.

Fortunately, the dispute had no lasting effect upon the transatlantic movement of wheat, and observers said again: "The Liverpool people are good traders and good customers." United Kingdom purchases from Canada continued with only small variations from year to year. Over the three decades ending in 1965, British imports of Canadian wheat averaged 98,000,000 bushels per year.

During the same thirty-year period, Japan was Canada's second best customer for wheat, followed by West Germany and Belgium and a score of smaller purchasers. Canadian wheat in a rather typical year went to Luxembourg, Switzerland, Venezuela, the Philippines, the Netherlands, South Africa, Czechoslovakia, Poland, Cuba, East Germany, Romania and

Bulgaria, as well as those countries mentioned previously. Canadian flour in the year 1966-67 went to eighty-eight different countries.

Then there were the big sales to new customers—surprise customers—like Communist China and Russia. After the years of the fifties, when world wheat supplies seemed to be gaining on demand, the announcements about big and unexpected sales to China and then to Russia made the best possible news for prairie people.

The important chain of events began early in 1961. Russia, in January of that year, bought 7,300,000 bushels of wheat and Czechoslovakia bought a similar amount. Such transactions were encouraging, but they were not big enough to relieve the Canadian surplus problem more than slightly. But on February 2, after a successful selling effort on the part of the Canadian Wheat Board, the Minister of Agriculture rose in the House of Commons to announce the first big wheat contract with Communist China. Food shortages had been acute in that country and China was taking 28,000,000 bushels of wheat and 12,000,000 bushels of barley for $60,000,-000—and paying cash. The announcement was greeted with both amazement and satisfaction. Few people entertained any thought of this unlikely customer returning to make more and bigger purchases. But the Chinese did want more wheat, and before the end of April in the same year, two contracts involving much bigger quantities of grain were signed, one for $66,000,000 worth of wheat, wheat flour and barley for 1961 delivery, and then—the monster undertaking on the part of China—for 157,000,000 bushels of wheat and 29,000,000 bushels of barley for something like $425,000,000. To farmers whose granaries and woodsheds and chicken-coops were full of wheat, it seemed too good to be true. But as time confirmed, the Chinese purchasers were anxious to have Canadian wheat and barley at prices which appeared entirely satisfactory to prairie growers.

Before the end of the 1960-61 crop year, 55,000,000 bushels of grain and flour had been shipped to Mainland China and in successive years the shipments were 91,000,000 bushels, 57,000,000 bushels, 56,000,000 bushels and 64,000,000 bushels, respectively.

Nor was the end in sight. On October 28, 1965, the Canadian Wheat Board announced the successful negotiation of a new three-year agreement with the Chinese grain-purchasing authority, covering delivery of from 112,000,000 to 186,000,000 bushels of wheat between August 1, 1966, and July 31, 1969. Then, meeting in 1966, both parties to the contract agreed to increase the amounts of wheat for delivery to a minimum of 168,000,000 bushels and maximum of 280,000,000 bushels.

Coming at a time when the Canadian wheat surplus was big and burdensome and crops were yielding far above the long-time average, the sales to China and other new customers were of the greatest benefit and importance.

Russia's entry as a large-scale purchaser of Canadian wheat came in 1963. Because of the biggest crop Canada had experienced, the need for additional market outlets was urgent. Just as agricultural people talked for years about the bumper crop of 1915, so the crop of 1963 promised to provide some lasting memories. The western soil yielded 703,000,000 bushels of wheat and the autumn seemed almost ideal for the big harvest. But how could such a huge volume of grain be sold? This amount of wheat added to a carry-over at August 1, 1963, of 487,000,000 bushels gave Canadians the enormous total of 1,190,000,000 bushels to sell, store or consume!

The urgent need for new market outlets was most apparent, and the new Russian deal seemed like the answer to prayers. It could not have come at a more propitious time. The 234,000,000 bushels bought by the Russians for roughly $500,000,000, coupled with increased sales to traditional customers like the United Kingdom, Japan and West Germany, brought Canadian wheat exports for the 1963-64 crop year to 594,000,000 bushels, almost twice as much as Canada had been sending abroad in an average year. Even the domestic demand of 156,000,000 bushels was higher than in the previous year so notwithstanding the record crop which might have brought serious storage and marketing problems, the country ended the crop year at July 31, 1964, with a smaller carry-over stock than was held at the beginning of the year.

After producing 703,000,000 bushels of wheat in 1963, the soil might have been expected to show exhaustion. Instead of that, it yielded 578,000,000 in 1964, then 661,000,000 in 1965 and 824,000,000 in 1966. That 1966 production represented a new record, big enough to overshadow completely what was considered a sensational output in 1963. The four-year total of 2,726,000,000 bushels—an average of 691,000,000 per year—was something which would have seemed fantastic in the thirties and almost fantastic in the forties and fifties.

The series of fruitful years added to the urgent importance of finding new markets, and again an unexpected wheat order of unprecedented magnitude came at the moment of greatest need. The purchase by Russia of $800,000,000 worth of Canadian wheat and flour, announced in Moscow, June 20, 1966, by Hon. Robert Winters of Canada's Department of Trade and Commerce, was said to be the biggest single commercial wheat transaction in the history of world trade. By the terms of the contract, signed on the previous day by the Chairman of the Canadian Wheat Board and the Chairman of the Russian Grain Importing Agency, the Soviet Union would take the equivalent of 336,000,000 bushels over a three-year period. It was sufficient to ensure an above-average annual export for the length of the contract and enough to make a big impact upon the entire Canadian economy.

In the words of the Minister of Trade and Commerce: "It will be felt not only by wheat farmers and millers but by grain handlers, longshoremen, elevator companies, railways, shipping companies and the economy generally." It was a further reminder of the importance of wheat to the nation, and a clear demonstration of the good fortune in finding new customers when they were needed.

CHAPTER XXXII

꙳

THE WORLD'S BEST

꙳

Western Canadians, never needlessly modest, have found very convincing reasons for believing they have the world's best wheat. Although the common wheat species is not native to the Western World, it flourished in the new Canadian soil and far surpassed the best it had been able to do in the Middle East where it was discovered.

The Canadian claim to having the best in wheat is one the competitors in other parts find difficult to challenge. International Grain Shows furnish part of the proof. In fifty-four World Championship contests between 1911 and 1968, Canadian exhibitors won the supreme award forty-nine times and western Canadian exhibitors won it forty-eight times. It is something to brag about.

The most important reason for international popularity of Canadian wheat is to be found in its supremely high quality for bread-making. The prairie areas produce some durum wheats, particularly well suited for making macaroni, but most varieties are of the hard, red, spring kinds, relatively rich in protein and favored by millers and bakers alike. Indicative of the importance attached to the protein fraction, some people in the grain trade are ready to use it as the principal basis for sales.

Protein has an essential place in both human and animal nutrition. No other food constituent can take its place in making and repairing muscle and performing certain body functions. Protein deficiency presents one of the most serious problems in feeding the world's masses. People in the more prosperous countries can draw upon meat and dairy foods to satisfy physiological needs, but those in many crowded and backward lands have to depend upon vegetable proteins. The fact that wheat carries more protein than rice can furnish, is of special importance.

For millers and bakers, however, there is an added significance in wheat protein. The protein, gluten, gives wheat dough its sticky and elastic character. This, in turn, makes it possible for dough, in the bread-making process, to rise and give a light and porous loaf. Gases generated by yeast organisms are trapped, and the doughy loaf has to expand.

The protein content of western Canadian wheat over the years averaged about 13.75 per cent. Rather commonly, it was lower in years of heavy rainfall, and higher in years of drought. Although wheat grown in the park belt where moisture is usually more favorable, outyields wheat from the plains, it cannot match the prairie product in sample and quality. Prairie wheats, hard, heavy, and rich in color, have the best grading record and the largest number of competition successes. Most exhibits winning major seed fair championships have come from fields in the Palliser Triangle, where soil and climate seem to combine to produce the positive best.

There are those countries where traditional habits and the need for economy have invited bread wheats of lower grades and quality, and there are those observers in the grain business who believe that Canada should have wheats to meet every need. But where people, like those in the United Kingdom, fancy clear white bread with good texture and the character of lightness, Canadian wheat is wanted. British millers, drawing wheat from many parts of the world, insist upon a certain amount of the Canadian product for use in their skillful blending operations.

Millers and bakers hold strong views, but the best public demonstrations of superiority are seen in the large number of times western Canadian growers and exhibitors have won the coveted World Championships.

Rev. John Gough Brick, from faraway Peace River district, won the high honor in 1893, but the success was not repeated for eighteen years and in the meantime, most people forgot and seemed ready to conclude that western growers were not ready for international competitions. That opinion, however, was to change. A new chapter in competition successes began when Seager Wheeler of Rosthern won the World Crown for wheat at New York in 1911. It brought fame to Wheeler, to Saskatchewan, and to the West. Repeating in 1914, 1915, 1916 and 1918, Wheeler had five championship successes and proved conclusively that his notable triumph in 1911 was more than an accident.

Herman Trelle of Wembley, Alberta, equaled the Wheeler record of five world championships, winning in 1926, 1930, 1931, 1932 and 1936. But the most significant point was the almost unbroken record of World Championships for western growers from the time the little Rosthern homesteader with the flare for crop improvement sent his entry of Marquis wheat to the New York Land Show.

The results of the recognized international shows in the United States for the years from 1911 to and including 1957, and of the winners of the coveted Canadian National Railways trophy at the Royal Agricultural Winter Fair, Toronto, from 1947 to 1968 provide a record to justify the pride of western growers. In more than fifty years during which world championship trophies have been offered — Canadian and American trophies overlap from 1947 to 1957 and during the war years from 1942 to 1945 there were no contests of international caliber — a Manitoba exhibitor won once; British Columbia growers won on five occasions; Saskatchewan entries won thirteen times, and Alberta entries, thirty-six times. Only in nine years did exhibitors from other parts win the coveted championship; an English exhibitor won in 1957 and an Ontario exhibitor in 1954. In the remaining seven years, winners were from the United States.

The year-by-year record of world championship winners deserves study. Winners at the International Grain and Hay Show, Chicago, were:

1911	Seager Wheeler, Rosthern, Saskatchewan.
1912	Henry Holmes, Raymond, Alberta.
1913	Paul Gerlach, Allan, Saskatchewan.
1914	Seager Wheeler, Saskatchewan.
1915	Seager Wheeler, Saskatchewan.
1916	Seager Wheeler, Saskatchewan.
1917	Samuel Larcombe, Birtle, Manitoba.
1918	Seager Wheeler, Saskatchewan.
1919	J. C. Mitchell, Dahinda, Saskatchewan.
1920	J. C. Mitchell, Saskatchewan.
1921	G. W. Kraft, Montana, United States.
1922	R. O. Wyler, Luseland, Saskatchewan.
1923	Maj. H. G. L. Strange, Fenn, Alberta.
1924	J. C. Mitchell, Saskatchewan.
1925	L. P. Yates, Montana, United States.
1926	Herman Trelle, Wembley, Alberta.
1927	C. Edson Smith, Montana, United States.
1928	C. Edson Smith, United States.
1929	J. H. B. Smith, Wolf Creek, Alberta.
1930	Herman Trelle, Alberta.
1931	Herman Trelle, Alberta.
1932	Herman Trelle, Alberta.
1933	Frank Isaacson, Elfros, Saskatchewan.
1934	John B. Allsop, Wembley, Alberta.

1935   W. Frelan Wilford, Stavely, Alberta.
1936   Herman Trelle, Alberta.
1937   Gordon Gibson, Ladner, British Columbia.
1938   F. Lloyd Rigby, Wembley, Alberta.
1939   F. Lloyd Rigby, Alberta.
1940   F. Lloyd Rigby, Alberta.
1941   William Miller, Edmonton, Alberta.
1942 to 1945, International Show discontinued because of war.
1946   Mrs. Amy Kelsey, Erickson, British Columbia.
1947   S. J. Allsop, Red Deer, Alberta.
1948   S. J. Allsop, Alberta.
1949   Mrs. Amy Kelsey, British Columbia
1950   R. P. Robbins, Shaunavon, Saskatchewan.
1951   Harold Metcalf, Fairgrove, Michigan, United States.
1952   Spencer Dunham, Caro, Michigan, United States.
1953   Fred W. Hallworth, Taber, Alberta.
1954   Elson Baur, Unionville, Michigan, United States.
1955   Jerry J. Leiske, Beiseker, Alberta.
1956   Jerry J. Leiske, Alberta.
1957   Jerry J. Leiske, Alberta.

The year 1957 was the last year the International Grain and Hay Show was held as a feature of Chicago's International Livestock Exposition.

World championship winners of the C.N.R. Trophy at Toronto's Royal Agricultural Winter Fair from 1947 to 1968 were:

1947   Mrs. A. G. Kelsey, Erickson, British Columbia.
1948   S. J. Allsop, Red Deer, Alberta.
1949   Mrs. A. G. Kelsey, British Columbia.
1950   Rickey Sharpe, Munson, Alberta.
1951   Howard Roppel, Rockyford, Alberta.
1952   Ronald R. Leonhardt, Drumheller, Alberta.
1953   Ronald R. Leonhardt, Alberta.
1954   W. E. Breckon, Burlington, Ontario.
1955   Robert Cochrane, Grande Prairie, Alberta.
1956   William Deurloo, Granum, Alberta.
1957   A. Davidson, Essex, England.
1958   Miss Gail Adams, Drumheller, Alberta.
1959   Douglas J. MacIntosh, Granum, Alberta.
1960   Wilbert Suehwold, Mitchellton, Saskatchewan.
1961   Ralph L. Erdman, Lethbridge, Alberta.

1962   Fred W. Hallworth, Taber, Alberta.
1963   George Luco, Lethbridge, Alberta.
1964   Lawrence Gibson, Carbon, Alberta.
1965   Larry Hixt, Beiseker, Alberta.
1966   Larry Hixt, Alberta.
1967   Larry Hixt, Alberta.
1968   Harold Hansen, Vulcan, Alberta.

The Rev. John Gough Brick sample, which won the world championship in 1893, was prepared for exhibition without benefit of any mechanical aids. To clean the grain, Brick simply tossed it in the air and let the Peace River breezes carry away the chaff and light seeds. That was all. Seager Wheeler's main help was from a hand-powered fanning mill. As time passed, the showing of grain became a highly specialized activity calling for patience and skill. Ultimately, most exhibitors resorted to hand picking to ensure freedom from impurities with only sound, plump and uniform kernels remaining. Nevertheless, anyone hoping to win a championship knows he has to start with a sample possessing outstanding merit. That is where exhibitors from the Canadian Prairies hold an advantage.

CHAPTER XXXIII

❧

THE WORLD'S GREAT NEED

❧

Custodians of one of the greatest expanses of wheatland in the world ought not to ignore the preachings of Thomas Robert Malthus,[46] the gloomy English churchman and economist, at whom people have laughed for over 160 years. According to his theory, expressed in "Essay On Population," 1798, the world's people would increase faster than the production of foodstuff. Without some restrictions upon population, mankind would face disaster in the form of mass starvation. What those who have scoffed at Malthus have overlooked is that such a phenomenon is fairly common in the animal world.

The cheerful ones have been quite confident that science would be the means of saving the race. And science did respond in an admirable manner. With agricultural advances, food producers appeared for a time to be keeping abreast with population; when world population increased by 2 per cent in a year, food production increased by the same percentage figure.

But some things have been ignored. Perhaps the periodic occurrence of a surplus of wheat or some other food commodity tended to veil the fact of the world's masses being close to starvation in one of its forms at the best of times. Moreover, there has been obvious famine in some part of the world almost constantly. Famine in China during one century, took an estimated hundred million lives. And for every individual dying from starvation, there have been scores—perhaps hundreds—suffering from malnutrition or "hidden hunger" in one of its many forms.

Nor is there any assurance that agricultural science can continue indefinitely to advance food production as it did during a few decades in the twentieth century. Successes on the farm scenes were, indeed, spectacular. Nobody would try to minimize them. The application of fertilizers helped to restore lands depleted by centuries of cropping; pesticides reduced the huge annual losses from weeds, insects and plant diseases; better methods of handling perishable foods resulted in delivery of fruits and vegetables with little deterioration and waste; use of synthetic hormones like stilbestrol raised the rate of gain in animals kept for meat; irrigation doubled the output from some dry fields; milk production per cow and egg production per hen were increased—sometimes by 100 per cent.

About the impact of new methods, there can be no doubt. Hens which increased their contribution from 100 eggs per year to 200, might have been expected to do still better. But limits have to be recognized. The law of diminishing returns is inescapable. Land suitable for the production of wheat and other foods is limited, and irrigation cannot be carried beyond the availability of water. Regardless of what those people who indulge in wishful thinking may say, it is difficult to see a burgeoning and unrestrained human family escaping indefinitely from some unprecedented experiences with hunger. It is too soon to say that Malthus was wrong. United States' President Johnson, speaking early in 1967, acknowledged that the battle against hunger was not going well. "Next to the pursuit of peace," said he, "the greatest challenge to the human family is in the race between food supply and population increases. That race is being lost."

Nobody can conscientiously dismiss the problems and dangers created by a population growth of more than a million, net, every week—more than a million extra people for meals every seven days. High rate of fertility—especially in Asiatic countries and Central America—and an accompanying drop in infant mortality have combined to produce the frightening "population explosion."

At the time of the prophet Malthus, world population was still less than one billion.[47] A hundred and sixty-five years later, it was at three billions, and scholars are talking about the prospect of six billions by the year 2000. The annual rate of increase is almost $2\frac{1}{2}$ per cent, giving rise to the awful thought that, without effective checks upon human numbers, the earth's land will provide "standing room only" in a few generations.

Those people who understand biological laws know that overpopulation will never reach the point of "standing room only" because, if humans fail to impose their own restraints, natural forces will certainly exercise effective and probably painful controls. Disease could be one of nature's cruel but effective ways of reducing human numbers, as it is one of nature's ways of reducing rabbits. And mass starvation could be another.

Food and Agriculture Organization officers, reporting in 1966, had nothing very cheerful to tell. World population in the previous year increased by seventy millions, they said, and available food per person was lower. In Asia, Africa and Latin America, with 60 per cent of the world's people, food production was actually lower by 2 per cent, and the world situation, as far as food was concerned, was described as precarious. Whether or not this was to be taken as a trend, the circumstances suggested a widening rather than a narrowing of the gap between population and available food supplies.

Canadians, with a favorable ratio between domestic population and food resources, may be the last to feel the misery of advancing world hunger, but they should know the folly of supposing they can isolate themselves from it. They know they will hear ever-clearer calls for food.

There are humanitarian and practical business reasons why Canadians should grasp every opportunity to declare their interest and willingness to participate in food programs. It would be the part of wisdom and decency to make the war against world hunger a primary international role. It could do nothing but good to declare: "Food is Canada's principal business. The agricultural 'assembly line' is long and efficient. Canadian producers can furnish quality to suit a king's taste. The country's facilities are capable of processing for any market. Canadians will trade with anybody."

The human instinct is to choose a diet made rich with high-protein foods of animal origin—meats, dairy products, and eggs. But such diets are costly, and of necessity, 75 per cent of the world's people have become vegetarians or near-vegetarians. An acre of wheat or rice or corn or potatoes can furnish more human food in terms of tonnage or calories than a similar area supporting beef cattle or pigs kept for meat. In other words, a given quantity of wheat or other grain eaten directly by humans will furnish at least twice as many calories of energy as the same amount of grain after it is converted to beef or pork or milk or cheese. Consequently, people facing hunger or famine cannot afford to eat much food of animal origin, and the most practical export programs designed for the relief of famine areas have to embrace the cereals—wheat, rice, barley and the like. Such cereals already furnish the principal part of diets in areas likely to need aid. Although they supply only one-quarter of the calories for Canadian and United States' diets, they are the source of three-quarters of the calories or food energy in the crowded and needy countries. The cereals alone cannot furnish perfect nutrition—not by any means—but most needy countries, hoping for the broadest and most economical relief, will invite wheat or rice or barley ahead of the more luxurious foods.

Canadian growers, quite often, have known discouragement when wheat was difficult to sell. Those times will come again, but with the growing number of world appetites and bread likely to be regarded as the basic food essential, the calls for wheat are bound to become more numerous. The pressure of population may eliminate meats and other foods costly to produce, but the need for cereals can only grow.

All the wheat Canada can produce will not end world hunger, but the wheat which can be spared for export will help. Whether the world food emergency be great or small, Canada's finest contribution will almost certainly be in terms of wheat.

CHAPTER XXXIV

THE RESOURCES FOR FOOD

The inheritance of soil has accounted for Canada's record in furnishing wheat and flour. Not that it is so extensive as some pronouncements have made it appear, but it is important enough to be considered the most valuable of all natural resources. Because of it, the West has been described as the "Granary of the World." And while wheat continues to move undiminished from the Granary, a mounting output of commercial fertilizer, such as is needed to make crops grow in other parts of the world, gives the country a dual role in bringing relief to hungry masses.

When essential fertilizers being exported are added to wheat exports, no doubt is left about the big part Canada can perform in the business of supplying food. Exporters can ask their customers: "What will you have? Do you want wheat or will it be potash and other fertilizers which will help you grow your own wheat?" Whichever is requested, it is bound to be an important aid in relieving a grave need.

Ninety-eight per cent of world food comes from soil. Unfortunately, there is not enough soil to provide for all needs, and it is not well distributed in relation to population. Asia, with half of the world's people, has only one-quarter of the food-producing soil; hence the necessity of restricting plantings to foodstuffs capable of furnishing the maximum of calories, even though quality and nutrition suffer.

Of the world's thirty-six billion acres of land surface, much is in regions which are climatically unsuited to cropping and 20 per cent is desert. Some is rocky terrain, leaving only about four billion acres from which the important part of man's food can be derived. Nor can the area of four billion acres be extended very much. It is inadequate enough in a world with three billion people to be fed; it can be seriously inadequate when population reaches six or ten or twenty billions. Available farm land at about one and one-third acres per person will provide a strictly vegetarian diet for three billion people, but cannot furnish a mixed diet such as people want and need. The importance of treating wheat soil, wherever it may be, as a commodity in short supply cannot be over-emphasized.

Canada's land area has been the envy of men in many parts. The 3,500,000 square miles of territory in a country with twenty million people represents 112 acres for every man, woman and child. That is more than any other country can offer. But total land space—no matter how much of an asset it may be otherwise—is not to be confused with agricultural or food-producing land. Canada, though fortunate in resources of soil, has less than an abundance of it. It is an error to suppose that a country with "great open spaces" will necessarily have "unlimited" lands awaiting development. When muskegs, rocks, and mountainous surfaces are deducted from the whole, the country has little enough of good and fertile soil.

The census of 1961 showed 103,000,000 acres of improved farm land in Canada, representing five acres per person. It was a high per capita acreage, perhaps the highest in the world. The United States, at the same time, had about three acres of improved crop land per person; Germany had three-quarters of an acre; France, one and one-half acres; China, less than half an acre; Japan, about one-quarter of an acre.

Canada's high per capita acreage of food-producing soil is explained by low population rather than by the "unlimited farm land" talked about by early promoters. But what will be the Canadian position when population reaches fifty millions, as it will at some time not far in the future? Will available crop land increase with population? The answer is: "No!"

Canadians are slow to realize that in spite of their country's huge area—second only to the Soviet Union—their good crop land represents less than 5 per cent of the total. New frontier areas to the north are becoming occupied, but they are generally small and largely offset by the encroachment of industries and highways and cities. The United States is said to be losing one million acres of farm land per year to other uses. Canadians can see big portions of their land in locations like the Fraser Valley and the Niagara Peninsula being snatched from food production. In the wheat country, land losses to non-agricultural uses are relatively small but they are significant.

Nobody can fail to miss the moral, that nothing is more important than good care for good soil, regardless of where it may be. Proper care means protection from wind and water erosion, protection from depletion of organic matter and elements of fertility, and protection against developers who would completely change its use.

Many times, there were warnings that western soil was being ruined. They deserved attention since resources did suffer from wind and water and repeated cropping. Fertility withdrawals were substantial. A forty-bushel-per-acre crop of wheat removes about forty-seven pounds of nitrogen, twenty-one pounds of phosphate and twelve pounds of potash, and without the application of fertilizer, the "bank account" of native fertility has to show a reduced "balance." Growing crops without provision for replacement of nutrients is like budgeting for deficits and spending capital.

A publication from the Department of Soil Science at the University of Saskatchewan reminds Canadians that: "Every bushel of grain, every pound of beef or gallon of milk sold off the farm means some removal of nitrogen, phosphorus and potassium and other mineral nutrients from the soil. Fifty years of cropping have already removed as much as 20 to 25 per cent of the original supply of nitrogen and phosphorus from Saskatchewan soils. No wonder our lands are beginning to respond to fertilizers."

The criticism directed at western wheat growers that they were "mining" their soil had a basis in validity, but the amazing point was that crop land continued to produce abundantly. The best yields came after decades of cropping when soils should have been showing signs of exhaustion.

When 1963 proved to be the biggest crop year in prairie history, many people said: "It can't happen again." But 1966 was a bigger one.

The big yields were due in part to the use of commercial fertilizers. Application of fertility from bags was almost unknown in prairie circles prior to World War II, but tests made a favorable case for nitrogen and phosphate in the chemical fertilizers and farmers recognized them as good investments. Manitoba, Saskatchewan and Alberta growers bought 61,837 tons of fertilizer for their 1956 crop, and for their 1966 crop, their purchases totaled 684,211 tons, an increase of over 1,000 per cent in ten years.

But even with the application of fertilizers, at levels of recent years, grain growing has become a deficit operation for the soil. In 1963, for example, when western fields yielded 703,000,000 bushels of wheat, 304,000,000 bushels of oats, 213,000,000 bushels of barley, 11,000,000 bushels of rye and 20,000,000 bushels of flax, the purchase and use of 289,834 tons of fertilizer went only part way in compensating for withdrawals of plant food. The total of 32,000,000 tons of grain harvested in that year would remove about 650,000 tons of nitrogen, 270,000 tons of phosphate and 170,000 tons of potash. What was returned in commercial fertilizer would represent roughly 8 per cent of the nitrogen in the grains harvested, 33 per cent of the phosphate and one-fifth of 1 per cent of the potash.

In spite of this substantial deficit, the Midwestern crop of the next year was almost as big. The crop of 1966 was bigger, reaching the unprecedented volume of 824,000,000 bushels of wheat, 253,000,000 bushels of oats, 279,000,000 bushels of barley and enough rye and flax to bring the three-province total to over 37,000,000 tons.

The potential of western crop land was never clearer. The amount of wheat available for export was never bigger. While Canadian wheat was moving at record rates, the manufacture and sale of fertilizer materials were becoming big business, with importance extending far beyond the country's boundaries. Overseas purchasers, who knew they could obtain wheat from Canada, discovered that they could obtain both wheat and those essential raw materials for home production. The export of food to impoverished nations is, in many instances, an interim solution. The more lasting relief has to be found by increasing production in the regions affected. Herein, Canada's fertilizers have much to offer.

The very area with well-established fame for wheat has become the scene of vigorous activity in mining and manufacturing fertilizers. The western provinces have most of the necessary materials. Sulphur, as a product from natural gas, is available in large amounts. Natural gas makes it possible for manufacturers to capture nitrogen from the atmosphere. Beneath Saskatchewan's wheat lands are found the most gigantic deposits of potash known to exist anywhere.

The only material lacking for a complete fertilizer manufacturing program is phosphate rock. Small deposits have been discovered in the Crow's Nest Pass, but until bigger ones are located, Canadian plants will be obliged to import from United States' mines. But manufacturers have not hesitated to import phosphate rock and use it in combination with Canadian materials for sales at home and abroad.

Millions of dollars have been invested in new plants and extensions to old ones. Big oil companies have been attracted to the fertilizer industry. Production has soared. As domestic use has increased, so has export. Canada's fertilizer exports passed the level of 1,000,000 tons for the first time in 1963. In 1966, exports totaled 3,772,221 tons and the grand total for exports and sales to Canadian users amounted to 5,690,085 tons. Almost half of the exports in the latter year were in the form of potash from Saskatchewan mines just getting started in production.

Who can guess the bread-making equivalent of those fertilizer exports or the bread equivalent of the wheat and fertilizer exports considered together? More and more, wheat and fertilizer for export appear like partners with a common purpose.

There is comfort in the thought that Canada's raw materials for fertilizer manufacture will be available for many decades, perhaps for hundreds of years. Long after oil and natural gas wells cease to produce, the prairie area will have potash for sale. It is equally important that the western wheat soil serve mankind for hundreds of years, or hopefully, forever.

Whether human population doubles in the following few decades or not, the good soil will lose none of its essential importance. The people who are caretakers of the soil have a moral responsibility to delay a Malthus-type disaster and to treat the great Canadian Food Factory in such manner that it will remain in production forever.

❧

CHAPTER XXXV

OUR DAILY BREAD

❧

The loaf of good bread is a crowning Canadian achievement, bearing the marks of plant breeders, machinery makers, grain growers, handlers, millers, and bakers. It can be round or oblong, white or brown, big or small, homemade or bakery-produced. But in every case, its goodness begins with clean, high-quality wheat of selected kind. It became a part of the Canadian diet and has never lost its prominence and importance. Its importance has gone far beyond the bounds of Canada.

National food habits differ about as much as national tongues. People of certain races consume much meat while others, by choice or necessity, eat little or none. Some are accustomed to diets enriched with dairy products and others are not so fortunate. Some fancy pickled grasshoppers or roasted ants while others prefer to suffer some hunger. Only one article of diet can be considered as almost universal in its appeal, and that is bread made from wheat flour. Rice exceeds wheat in total amount eaten, but bread from wheat flour is still the most universal of all foods.

Many of the world's people eat bread and little else from reasons of necessity. Others eat it because they like it. In any case, they eat it. Moreover, it is a good food, possessing more of nutritional balance than many people realize. Its high carbohydrate content, giving high energy value, is recognized. But bread contains much more; it carries between 8 and 10 per cent of protein and over 1 per cent of mineral matter. Some breads are high in vitamins of the B complex. Thus, bread is capable of going far in meeting body requirements for the essential constituents.

The making and eating of bread from wheat appears to be as old as civilization. Samples of wheat found in ancient Egyptian tombs were placed there 5000 years ago, and no doubt, Egyptian homemakers of the period were proficient in making bread of one kind or another. During the "seven lean years" mentioned in the Book of Genesis, the Egyptians "cried to Pharaoh for bread."

The Patriarch, Abraham, served bread and wine to his guests and when Lot, Abraham's nephew, had visitors, he "made them a feast, and did bake unleavened bread and they did eat." And when Joseph's brothers came down into Egypt and a banquet was ordered, Joseph, occupying a high position in the administration of the country, commanded: "Set on bread."

No doubt, the bread of those early times was a dark and heavy product, with none of the porous texture seen in modern white loaves. Primitive flour made by crushing or grinding grain between stones might be described more correctly as a coarse meal. With all parts of the kernels present, it would be nutritious but it could not escape the dark color.

The Romans, by sifting the ground wheat with cloth screens, thereby removing the bran, were the first to produce a white flour and then a white bread. The removal of bran and germ did nothing to improve food value, but white bread had its own peculiar appeal, and as time went on, milling methods were adapted to make separation of the various parts of the kernel complete. Ultimately, millers were able to recover about forty-three pounds of really white flour from sixty pounds of wheat.

Even in modern times, breads have appeared in scores of forms and not all of them have owed their origin to wheat. But there is something distinctively superior about wheat flour for making bread of the light or raised or leavened kind. The leavening is achieved by adding yeast to the dough and giving the organisms a favorable temperature in which to do their work. It explains why bread making in either a farm kitchen or a commercial bakery demands time; the bread dough has to "rise" before baking. The yeast organisms, acting upon sugars and starches, generate carbon dioxide gas, and when trapped in the elastic dough, cause the loaf to expand or rise. But the only doughs with enough elasticity to expand and hold the gases are those made from flour having a high content of the protein, gluten. This explains one of the big advantages of wheat as a source of flour for bread, especially wheat such as is grown in western Canada.

The flat and heavy and unleavened bread continues to be eaten in many parts of the world, but western hemisphere preference points directly at the light and palatable loaf made with white flour and yeast.

After the dough has a chance and time to rise, the "bloated" loaves are placed in ovens for baking. The heat destroys the yeast bodies but cooks the bread without loss of the numerous pockets made by the gas. The result is the typical light loaf with porous texture.

In earlier years in Canada, every housewife made bread and found pride in the big and fluffy loaves she turned out. The kitchen odor of fresh bread was something to stimulate appetites. But in the march of time, bread making came more and more into the hands of commercial bakeries, turning out twenty-ounce loaves of good quality.

Wheat flour is not the only ingredient needed to make bread but it is the principal one. It takes the flour from approximately one pound of wheat to make a twenty-ounce loaf. It is apparent, therefore, that the cost of flour is not a big factor in determining the retail price of bread. When bread prices were advanced about two cents per loaf across the country in 1966, wheat growers were strongly critical of those bakery organizations which offered the "increased cost of ingredients" as justification. Wheat flour was, indeed, the main ingredient, but as an Alberta Wheat Pool statement was to explain, although bread prices to consumers had virtually doubled between the crops of 1945 and 1964, the farm price received for wheat was "almost exactly the same" in the two years. "At the present time," the editor of the *Wheat Pool Budget* wrote in March, 1966, "the farmer receives approximately 2.6 cents from the price of every loaf of bread that sells for up to 27 cents."

The main point in the Wheat Pool argument was that even "one cent a loaf on bread, if passed on to the farmer, would increase the price of his wheat by 60 cents a bushel." If an extra two cents per loaf—the amount by which the bakeries were increasing the price of bread at the time—were to be returned to the producers who also were being squeezed by greatly increased costs, the advance would have meant an additional $1.20 per bushel for that part of their wheat consumed in Canada.

With per capita consumption of bread averaging about one hundred pounds annually, it takes approximately forty million bushels of wheat to provide Canadians with that food product alone. Producing the raw materials for a nation's bread should be seen as the most essential and crucial of all occupational undertakings. And if there are advances in the price of bread, the wheat growers cannot be blamed for thinking they are entitled to some part of them.

The arguments about prices and returns continued and are likely to continue. Fortunately, the production of wheat and flour and bread continued and is likely to continue, also.

The story of wheat on the soils of western Canada began with the valiant efforts to make it grow. For a century and more it was a story marked by disappointments, failures, struggles and triumphs. It is a story that will have no end so long as human consumers choose to eat bread.

REFERENCE NOTES

[1] Captain John Palliser, an Irishman by birth and engineer by training, was the leader of the first scientific party to conduct a study of the Canadian Prairies and Park Belt. Appointed by the Imperial Government, he and members of his well-qualified group spent the summers of 1857, 1858 and 1859 in Rupert's Land. The Palliser Report had a big impact upon government policy. The area enclosed in what became known as the Palliser Triangle was considered to be an extension of the Great American Desert and too dry for settlement and farming. The base of the Triangle was along the International Boundary from a point roughly south of Fort Macleod to a point southwest of Brandon, while the apex would be close to the location of Lloydminster (see map). In the so-called Fertile Belt, northward from the Triangle, however, Palliser found reasons for enthusiasm.

[2] John Macoun, an early traveler and writer in the West, was more optimistic than Palliser and his book *Manitoba and The Great North-West,* published in 1882, helped to bring settlers into the country. He had been professor of botany at Albert College in Belleville until his appointment to serve as botanist with the Sandford Fleming Expedition to the West in 1872. After successive journeys across the West in advance of the railway, Macoun wrote his famous book, establishing himself as the first to recognize the tremendous stores of fertility in western soils, prairie soils as well as parkland.

[3] The Dominion Lands Act was passed in 1872. It, and the orders in council which followed, provided for the allotment of lands for homesteading and grazing. Males over 21 years who were British subjects or declared their intention of becoming British subjects—also widows—were entitled to file on homestead quarter sections.

[4] Hon. Ian Mackenzie, who was first elected to the House of Commons in 1930, was a close associate of Prime Minister Mackenzie King and served in various capacities in Liberal cabinets, first as Minister of National Defence in 1935 and, near the end of World War II, as Minister of Veterans' Affairs, although his health had been poor for some time. He died September 2, 1949.

[5] "Emmer" and "spelt" are close relatives of common wheat but differ in that the heads of both break up into spikelets at threshing and retain their chaff. Emmer and spelt have never been grown extensively in Canada.

[6] Chevalier de la Corne, following the la Vérendryes by only a few years, paddled westward on the Saskatchewan and halted to build a trading post on the south side of the river, about due north of where the town of Kinistino exists today. Carrying the French founder's name, this fort was, for a while, the most westerly in the French chain of trading posts and was seen as a major obstacle to the dreams of British traders inviting the Indians to take their furs to them on Hudson's Bay. The French competition forced the Hudson's Bay Company people to establish trading sites at inland places.

[7]Peter Pond, a tempestuous New Englander and one of the founders of the North West Company, went over the Methye Portage to establish a post on Athabasca River in 1778. There he earned the distinction of being the first white man to cultivate and plant domestic seeds in what is now the province of Alberta. The place of planting was about 30 miles upstream from Lake Athabasca. Alexander Mackenzie, prior to his trip north on the river now bearing his name, saw potatoes, cabbages, turnips and carrots growing on Pond's land beside the post.

[8]The Earl of Selkirk (1771-1820), from whom the first colony of farming people in the West took its name, had demonstrated unusual sympathy for evicted Scottish crofters. It was with the idea of establishing a colony that he accepted a grant of 116,000 square miles of land, including portions of present-day Manitoba, Saskatchewan, Minnesota and North Dakota. Previously he assisted settlements in Prince Edward Island and Upper Canada, but the plan for the Red River area was by far his biggest undertaking. Sending settlers to Rupert's Land at that time was considered both bold and dangerous.

[9]Miles Macdonell had come out from Scotland to New York State as a boy, not long before the Revolutionary War. He had then been brought to Canada in the Loyalist migration and in due course had become a soldier and had risen to the rank of captain in the Canadian Volunteers. On the disbandment of his corps in 1802, Miles had taken to farming at Osnabruck, just west of Cornwall in Upper Canada. There, he met Lord Selkirk for the first time in 1804, and Selkirk was much impressed by his ambition and boldness. The voyage to Red River, to take over the grant of 116,000 square miles, in the name of Lork Selkirk, from the Hudson's Bay Company, had been filled with disasters from its beginning. Macdonell's experiences at Red River continued to be trying and at one point he was made a prisoner by the North West Company men and taken to Lower Canada for trial. Before Selkirk's death in 1820, Macdonell had put in a claim for £4,400 for overdue wages and compensation for lost earnings. When he learned that Selkirk was prepared to allow £500, he abandoned the claim and lived his few remaining years on the charity of his brother at Point Fortune on the Ottawa River.

[10]Fort Gilbraltar, the North West Company post, was at the mouth of the Assiniboine River and within the limits of the modern city of Winnipeg. Pembina was at the mouth of the Pembina River, just south of the present International Boundary.

[11]Alexander Ross, known as the Red River Historian, came into the Hudson's Bay Company service following the Union with the North West Company in 1821. George Simpson sent him from the West Coast to Red River to become a teacher. There, upon his retirement, he wrote two books dealing with the fur trade and his better-known book entitled *Red River Settlement,* published by Smith, Elder and Co., London, 1856.

[12]The exact Métis population of 1815 is unknown. When Manitoba's first census was taken in 1870, it showed 9,848 Métis and 1,563 whites.

[18]Colin Robertson was accompanying a party of Hudson's Bay Company men destined for Athabasca when he discovered the sad plight of Red River settlers following the attack of 1815. He remained at Red River and succeeded in inducing the settlers who had taken flight to return to their riverside homes. Under his leadership, the colony was rehabilitated but only temporarily because the more severe blow fell in the following year.

[14]Seven Oaks, site of the massacre on June 19, 1816, and at which Governor Semple and his followers were cut down by Cuthbert Grant's men, was about two miles north of Fort Douglas. The Métis group following Grant rode in from the west, roughly along an extension of what is now Portage Avenue in Winnipeg, and when a short distance from the settlement, the riders veered to the northeast. Semple and his men rode north along the trail which corresponds to modern Main Street and met up with the well-armed Métis where the battle took place.

[15]The career of Seager Wheeler, noted plant breeder and winner of many world wheat championships, is discussed in chapter XVII, "First Links in a Chain of Championships."

[16] "City Datum" at Winnipeg is computed from a low-water benchmark, 727.57 feet above sea level, at the James Avenue pumping station, as determined by the Geodetic Survey of Canada; it is used in reckoning river flood levels.

[17] Alexander Ross, *Red River Settlement*, p. 116.

[18] Sir Archibald Alison (1792-1867) was a British lawyer and historian, author of *History of Europe* in 10 volumes.

[19] John Henry Lefroy, when called to give evidence before the Select Committee of the Imperial House of Commons on February 23, 1857, introduced himself as Inspector-General of Army Schools, also as one who had seen much of Red River Settlement and Rupert's Land.

[20] See reference No. 1.

[21] Louis Riel, leader of the western insurrections of 1869-70 and 1885, was French on his mother's side and Métis on his father's. Born beside the Red River in 1844, he attended school in Montreal, intending to enter the priesthood. But before his studies were completed, his father died and the young man returned to Red River to be with his widowed mother. Rather naturally, he became the Métis leader and tried to establish a home-spun government at Red River in 1869. After the collapse of his provisional administration, Riel was elected to the House of Commons but not allowed to take his seat. Again elected by voters in his Manitoba constituency, he was outlawed by vote of parliament and went to the United States where he was teaching school when the troubled Métis on the South Saskatchewan called him back some years later. He and Gabriel Dumont directed the fateful uprising of 1885. When the insurgents met defeat, Riel surrendered. He faced trial at Regina and was convicted and sentenced to be hung.

[22] Fort Macleod was the North West Mounted Police outpost, located on the Oldman River, about 100 miles south of where Calgary emerged later. It was named for Assistant Commissioner James Macleod—later Commissioner Macleod—who led the force to the spot.

[23] See reference No. 21.

[24] Treaty Number Seven was the last of the major treaties with prairie Indians and considered the most important. Participating were Blackfoot, Blood, Piegan, Stoney and Sarcee tribes and, because the Indians of the Southwest were believed to be the most ferocious, this treaty, signed at Blackfoot Crossing on the Bow, Sept. 22, 1877, was seen as a special triumph. Chief Crowfoot of the Blackfoot emerged as the undisputed Indian leader.

[25] Bishop Taché arrived at Red River as Frère Taché in 1845. A short time later he was ordained a priest by Bishop Provencher. In due course he became Bishop Taché and ultimately Archbishop Taché. During the period of the Riel insurrection at Red River, 1869-70, he was a most influential figure, respected by both Métis and members of the Government at Ottawa. He was one of the appointed members of the first Board of Education in Manitoba.

[26] See reference No. 21.

[27] "N.E. 35-12-7" would mean the northeast quarter of section 35 in a township which was in the 12th horizontal row from the International Boundary and in the 7th vertical row of townships numbering from the Principal Meridian to the East. This particular quarter was on the Portage Plains.

[28] See reference No. 2.

[29] The Barr Colony was the dream of Rev. Isaac Barr whose appeal to prospective settlers from England proved rather overwhelming. Many of those immigrants who took passage on the two ships chartered by Barr in the spring of 1903 were from the heart of London and total strangers to farming and frontier hardship. Saskatoon residents saw them arriving early in April and taking up temporary quarters in tents. Saskatoon was the end of the rail journey and there the would-be farmers

bought oxen, wagons, equipment and supplies for the 200-mile journey by trail to their "promised land" on the 4th meridian, where Lloydminster was built later. The size of the enterprise proved too much for Barr and his role as leader fell to Rev. Exton Lloyd, later Bishop Lloyd.

30 Adam MacKenzie was Manitoba's biggest farm operator. Most of his land was in the Arden district, northeast of Carberry.

31 Fort Ellice was a Hudson's Bay Company fort, built in 1831. It was on the upper Assiniboine River, close to the mouth of the Qu'Appelle.

32 The Qu'Appelle Valley cuts across the province of Saskatchewan from a point close to the Elbow of the South Saskatchewan and drains into the Assiniboine at Lazare, Manitoba. The Valley is noted for its beauty and legends.

33 H. G. L. Strange, an Englishman who served with the rank of Major in World War I, came to Canada in 1919 and engaged in farming at Fenn, Alberta. In 1923 he won the world's championship for wheat. In 1930 he was made director of the Research Department of the Searle Grain Company in Winnipeg, and his regular reports won wide recognition in agricultural circles. He died in Nov., 1964.

34 William Saunders (1836-1914) was a druggist in London, Ontario, where his five sons were born, and owned an orchard close to the town. A man with no formal education, he came to be regarded as the foremost authority in Canada on all matters pertaining to agriculture and horticulture. His work in cereal breeding was carried on by his son Charles (1867-1937), who was knighted for his contribution to agriculture. The Saunders became known as "the Marquis wheat family." In 1947, a variety originated at the Ottawa experimental farm was given the name Saunders. William Saunders had recommended the establishment of the Canadian Experimental Farm System in a report to the House of Commons in 1886, and he was appointed to the office of first director.

35 Seager Wheeler's homestead beside the South Saskatchewan River was 18 miles northeast of Saskatoon. After proving up on the homestead, he bought the Rosthern farm from the C.P.R. for $3 per acre.

36 Charles Hatfield, better known as Hatfield the Rainmaker, was the center of attraction around Medicine Hat in 1921. Farmers and ranchers, plagued by successive drought years, were ready to gamble and invited this man who had conducted some private researches in California and claimed to have discovered a rain-making technique. According to the deal made, Hatfield was to receive credit for half the rainfall between May 1 and August 1 and collect up to $8,000 for a maximum of four inches of rain. The basis of payment would be $4,000 per inch attributed to his efforts. Hatfield arrived April 20, 1921, and set up some mysterious equipment about 20 miles northeast of the Hat. With luck working for him, rains fell almost immediately and Hatfield was ready to take all the credit. June was a wet month but July was dry and farmers became angry. Hatfield claimed the maximum payment but settled for less. A few farmers wanted to give him another chance in 1922, but Hatfield did not come back.

37 Andrew Meikle built his threshing machine in 1786, the first to resemble a more modern thresher. In constructing it, Meikle employed a revolving drum and beaters, thus combining in principle the blow of the flail and some of the rubbing effect of the old threshing floor.

38 "Futures" trading is a market arrangement to permit speculation in grain or other commodities. Purchasers can contract to buy and sellers to deliver at specified dates in the future and at stated prices. It has been claimed that such trading brings stability to markets but, as stated by Bob Edwards (*Eye Opener*, Feb. 10, 1912): "All the speculation in the world never raised a bushel of wheat."

39 Rochdale in England was the scene of a notable pioneer experiment in co-operation. There, in 1844, residents opened a small food store and stocked it from funds subscribed by its supporters. The undertaking brought economies as well as lessons in co-operation and other communities followed the example. The distinctive fea-

tures of the Rochdale plan became basic principles in consumer co-operation: no member to hold more than one share of capital and dividends to be paid in proportion to the value of goods purchased.

40 The Union Government was a wartime administration under Prime Minister Sir Robert Borden. The necessity of compulsory military service and greater war effort generally led to the coalition in 1917. The Government continued beyond the end of World War I. Sir Robert Borden resigned as Prime Minister in 1920 and was followed in office by Arthur Meighen who continued until defeated in 1921.

41 Aaron Sapiro was a California lawyer who had been both active and successful in organizing producer co-operatives in the United States. When the proposal to organize Wheat Pools was being debated in 1923, Sapiro accepted the invitation to address meetings in the Canadian wheat belt. His electrifying influence was felt immediately. But he did not escape bitter controversy.

42 James Gardiner of Saskatchewan (1883-1962) had one of the longest records for public service in Canada. Born in Ontario, he obtained his education in the West and taught school before turning to farming at Lemberg and to politics. First elected to the Saskatchewan Legislature in 1914, he was premier of the province from 1926 to 1929 and from 1934 to 1935. He then entered federal politics and was Minister of Agriculture for Canada from 1935 to 1957.

43 Henry Youle Hind who caught the first vision of a dam at the Elbow of the South Saskatchewan River had been professor of chemistry and geology at the University of Trinity College when appointed by the Government of the Province of Canada in 1857 to conduct a study of the resources and opportunities in the West. He did not get beyond the limits of the present province of Manitoba in the first year but spent most of the second year in what is now Saskatchewan.

44 John Maynard Keynes (1883-1946) was educated at Cambridge and held important positions in the British Civil Service. He was frequently in controversy because of unorthodox views about economics. Governments, he believed, had to play a big part in stimulating the economy through public investment.

45 The European Common Market, with France, West Germany, Italy, Belgium, the Netherlands and Luxembourg as members, was created to gain mutual trading benefits through reduction and ultimate elimination of custom tariffs. The treaty by which the intention was confirmed was signed in Rome on March 25, 1957.

46 Thomas Malthus (1766-1834) was an English economist whose theories about population roused widespread discussion. The famous Malthusian doctrine was contained in "An Essay on the Principle of Population as It Affects the Future Improvement of Society," published in 1798. Revised editions followed but the conclusion was consistently gloomy, that population would eventually outgrow all means of subsistence.

47 A billion by United States and Canadian acceptance is a thousand millions (1,000,-000,000); but by English interpretation it is a million millions (1,000,000,000,000). In this work, a billion has been used to indicate a thousand millions and a trillion to mean a thousand billions or a million millions.

INDEX

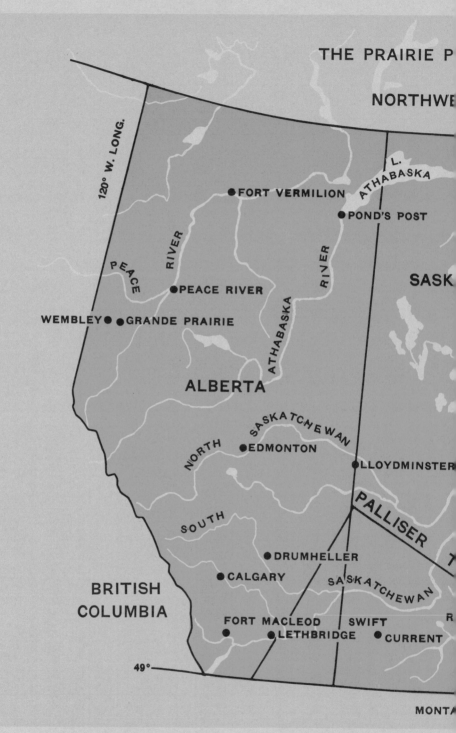

THE PRAIRIE P

NORTHWE

120° W. LONG.

L. ATHABASKA

● FORT VERMILION

● POND'S POST

PEACE

RIVER

RIVER

ATHABASKA RIVER

● PEACE RIVER

WEMBLEY ● ● GRANDE PRAIRIE

SASK

ALBERTA

SASKATCHEWAN

NORTH

● EDMONTON

● LLOYDMINSTER

SOUTH

PALLISER T

● DRUMHELLER

● CALGARY

SASKATCHEWAN

BRITISH
COLUMBIA

FORT MACLEOD ● SWIFT

● ● LETHBRIDGE ● CURRENT

R

49°

MONTA